Dr David Delvin is probably  writer in the UK, and has a lo well. TV credits include eight PEBBLE MILL AT ONE, plus BBC's MEDICAL EXPRESS and INSIDE MEDICINE, and ITV's THE GOOD SEX GUIDE. It was as resident medic at Anglia TV that he met and fell in love with his wife (and co-author of this book) Christine Webber.

His books have now sold over a million worldwide, and have been translated into ten languages. He won the 'Best Book' Award of the American Medical Writers' Association for *The Book of Love*, and was later awarded the Médaille de la Ville de Paris by Jacques Chirac.

He has written for many magazines and newspapers, and does a regular humour column for BMA NEWS REVIEW. He recently retired from the General Medical Council, after fifteen years as an elected member.

Christine Webber is an Agony Aunt on the TV satellite channel *UK Living*, and for the *Daily Star* newspaper. She spent twelve years as the leading presenter on Anglia TV, researching, writing and producing programmes on medical and social issues, and helping viewers with their problems. She is the author of a romantic novel and four sex education booklets. In an earlier life, she played Principal Boy in pantomimes and was lead singer with the 'Black & White Minstrels'. . .

The Big 'O'

Understanding and Improving Your
Orgasm and Your Partner's

Dr David Delvin and Christine Webber

NEW ENGLISH LIBRARY
Hodder and Stoughton

ACKNOWLEDGEMENTS

In our researches for this book, we have read every paper on orgasm which has been published in major medical journals during the last twenty years. We'd like to thank all the libraries which have found them for us and, in particular, Wendy Lopatin – librarian *extraordinaire*.

We also thank Charlotte —— of Edinburgh University, and Penelope Dunn of A.P. Watt Ltd, who so kindly sent out vast numbers of questionnaires.

Thanks, too, to the following organisations whose viewers, listeners and readers took part in our sex survey: UK Living TV, London News Radio, Scot FM, BBC Radio Scotland, *The Guardian* Women's Page.

Finally, our most grateful thanks to the 1032 women and men who helped us with our survey. All their contributions have been made anonymous.

First published in Great Britain in 1995 by Hodder & Stoughton

A division of Hodder Headline PLC
A New English Library paperback

10 9 8 7 6 5 4 3 2 1

Illustrations © Patricia Ludlow

British Library Cataloguing in Publication Data
Delvin, David
    Big O: Understanding and Improving Your Orgasm and Your
    Partner's
    I. Title   II. Webber, Christine
    III. Ludlow, Pat
    613.96

ISBN 0 340 63809 5

Typeset Avocet Typeset, Brill, Bucks
Printed and bound in Great Britain by
Cox & Wyman Ltd., Reading for
Hodder and Stoughton
A Division of Hodder Headline PLC
338 Euston Road
London NW1 3BH

CONTENTS

- The Myth
- The Reality
- What Actually IS an Orgasm?
- The Need for Gentle Preparation
- What a Woman Looks Like (and Sounds Like) During Orgasm
- Breasts During Orgasm
- Limbs During Orgasm
- Bottom During Orgasm
- Vulva and Clitoris During Orgasm
- Vagina During Orgasm
- Womb During Orgasm
- Feelings During Orgasm
- What are the Common Ways in Which Women Reach Orgasm?
- Masturbation
- Vibrators
- Hand Petting ('Touching Up')
- Cunnilingus
- Intercourse
- Multiple Orgasms
- Do Women Ejaculate During Orgasm?
- The Female G-spot and Orgasm
- Orgasm and Conception

- The Habit of Faking
- Alcohol and Drugs
- Fatigue
- The 'I Don't Orgasm' Syndrome

- Realise You're Not Alone
- Your Body and You
- Pleasure Yourself
- Now You Can Do It, Do It With Him
- Doing It During Intercourse

- Yes, You *can* Have Better Orgasms, and More of Them
- Get Yourself the Right Man For the Job
- Get Him to Read Chapter Ten
- Make Sure You Make Time For Yourself
- Always *Tell* Him What You Want in Bed
- Exercise Your PC Muscle
- Get Your Man To Use the 'Dual Approach' to Orgasm
- Use Fantasy
- Don't Hesitate To 'Touch Yourself Up'
- Buy a Vibrator
- Letting Yourself Have Multiple Orgasms
- Use the Famous CAT – and the PUSSY

- Yes, You *Can* Help Her
- Be Clean, Be Romantic and Kiss Her!
- Take Your Time
- Keep an Eye on Her Calendar
- Compliment Her – Especially on Her Vulva
- Consider the 'Ladies Come First' Rule

Chapter Sixteen: HOW TO GIVE YOUR MAN BETTER
ORGASMS: – A GUIDE FOR WOMEN   313

INTRODUCTION

Whether you're a woman or a man, orgasms are natural, normal – and probably good for your health. Having them regularly is nothing to be ashamed of!

Furthermore orgasms are *lovely*. Puritanically minded people *hate* this fact – which is why the Big 'O' was almost never mentioned in newspapers and magazines, or on TV or radio, until quite recent years. Some romantic and erotic novels dared to mention 'coming', but this was a very good way to get prosecuted . . .

Now things have changed and it's socially acceptable to talk about having climaxes. Some people even chat about it at dinner parties, though we do *not* recommend this! We were once present at a dinner where the host greatly embarrassed nearly everybody by announcing that his mistress – a world-famous actress – could come in four minutes flat. (Is this physically possible? Read on and you'll find out.)

So in this book we can be totally frank about the whole subject of male and female climaxes, and about the latest scientific research into them. You may be surprised to hear that experts are *still* researching orgasm, but they are. You see, the fact is that there's an awful lot that doctors and scientists still don't know about human climaxes. Because this subject was taboo for centuries, virtually no medical research was devoted to it till lately. As a result, doctors know more about things like (say) toenails than they do about orgasms.

However, researchers have learned a lot in the last twenty years or so, and nearly every month it is possible to find a worthwhile paper about some aspect of the human orgasm in a reputable medical journal – which is just as well, considering the vast number of people who have some difficulty with 'fetching off'!

So in this book we present the most up-to-date knowledge now available about the agreeable subject of reaching a climax. We'll tell you about:

- the way orgasms start in young people;
- how orgasms change during life;
- how they vary in intensity on different occasions;
- how to *increase* the intensity if you want to, for instance by using techniques which stimulate the female 'S-zone', recently described by Dr Delvin.

We'll also explain:

- the stages of orgasm;
- the *control* of orgasm – useful if you're someone (usually, but not always, male) who comes a bit too soon;
- the various ways of helping yourself or your partner to reach orgasm easily – something many women, and some men, find pretty difficult!

We'll tell you the truth about much misunderstood subjects, such as:
- multiple orgasm in women *and* men, including the results of our new survey;
- female ejaculation (i.e., 'squirting') during orgasm;
- orgasm induced by nipple stimulation;
- the relationship between orgasm and conception.

The Big 'O' is of course intended to help you learn more about your bodies, and to assist you in overcoming any sexual inhibitions and difficulties you may have. But above all, we hope that reading this book will be *fun* for you! It could well be that you and your partner would like to go through it *together*, experimenting with the techniques mentioned, and seeing if they bring pleasure to the pair of you. For, after all, orgasm should be an experience of pure pleasure. It is far and away the most *intensely* pleasurable sensation which your body can give you – better than enjoying the most delicious food or wine, and infinitely preferable to boring things like inhaling rotten old nicotine, or filling yourself up with other drugs!

By the way, if you're one of the diminishing band of disapproving people who still think that there's something 'wrong' with orgasmic pleasure, then this volume is probably not for you . . .

To everybody else, please have a great time with this book and – with a bit of luck – give and receive quite a few orgasms during the time you're reading it!

One final word: in our other books we've repeatedly stressed that orgasm shouldn't be a goal in itself. We remain firm in the view that there are other things which are more important in bed – things like love, romance, companionship, tenderness and (perhaps above all) laughter.

But, just for once, this particular book is *not* about those things. It is purely and simply about orgasms. So come on in!

And next, our orgasmic survey. Please read on . . .

OUR SURVEY

As part of our researches for *The Big 'O'*, we carried out a massive 'orgasm survey.'

It's easy to make fun of sex surveys – but they are actually the best way to get a 'snapshot' of people's sexual behaviour, rather than just relying on anecdotal evidence.

And we're pleased to say that our survey has produced some astonishing new facts – particularly about the sheer *difficulty* which the average woman has in reaching a climax. Late twentieth-century society has taken it as read that a female should be able to 'come' at the drop of a hat. Our survey shows that this just isn't true.

Now we have to admit that all sex surveys – including ours – are *bound* to be inaccurate!

The main reason for this is pretty obvious. People who are not remotely interested in sex do not fill in sexual questionnaires – in the same way that folk who don't drive are unlikely to participate in research on cars. Therefore, the 'study population' of a sex survey is largely made up of people who lead reasonably active love lives, although a minority of men and women who take part will actually do so because they are unhappy with their sex lives, and quite understandably want to tell someone about it.

Fortunately, in the 1990s there have been three very large-scale national surveys (in America, Britain and France) which have employed careful scientific techniques to try to avoid this bias. We pay tribute to them here; they are the massive University of Chicago Survey *The Social Organization of Sexuality*, by Laumann, Michael, Gagnon and Michaels; the authoritative British 'Wellcome' report (*Sexual*

Attitudes and Lifestyles, by Johnson, Wadsworth, Wellings and Field; published by Blackwell Scientific Publications); and the excellent *Analyse des Comportements Sexuels en France*, by Spira *et al*, published by *Agence Nationale de Recherches sur le Sida*, and INSERM.

We don't claim that our own survey is as scientifically designed as these three. But its great virtue is that it *concentrates solely on orgasms* – something which no other modern survey has done. And by homing in purely on orgasms, we have been able to make one or two remarkable discoveries – like the fact that so many women prefer the orgasms of love play to those of intercourse (men do NOT share this view!).

What is really striking is that most of the females who responded to our questionnaire said that:

* they could not climax at will (as men can);
* they regarded themselves as 'slow to come' – and found this worrying.

What this means is that a very large section of the female population has somehow been made to feel itself 'inadequate' in bed, simply because they cannot climax with the speed that men can.

We suggest that gentleman readers, in particular, should bear this finding in mind, next time they are urging a lady partner to climax.

And now to the main results of our survey.

PART ONE: FEMALES

First orgasm

The commonest age of first orgasm in our survey of women was eighteen. However, there was a very wide range, from five years of age (which may surprise you) up to forty. It's worth noting that the most common age of first *intercourse* was seventeen – which is a year before the age of first orgasm.

First *petting* most commonly took place at the age of fourteen, though this was often nothing more than a (definitely non-orgasmic) quick fondle of the breasts.

How was the first orgasm achieved?

Most people probably imagine that a female's 'orgasmic awakening' is at the hands of a man. We find that today that is quite untrue, the most common way in which a female reaches her first climax is through 'self-pleasuring'.

MASTURBATION	47%
SEXUAL INTERCOURSE	32%
PETTING	20%
WHILE SLEEPING	1%

How do women mainly climax *today*?

If, like many people, you believe that straightforward sexual intercourse should be enough to 'bring a woman off', then you're in for a shock! Our findings show quite clearly that only a minority of females regularly climax through 'unaided' sexual intercourse, with no clitoral stimulation. The main ways in which women reach orgasm are:

INTERCOURSE WITH NO ADDED STIMULATION	13%
CLITORIS STIMULATION DURING LOVE PLAY OR INTERCOURSE	75%
MASTURBATION	12%

Climaxing through love play

Happily, 88 per cent of our female respondents said that they can orgasm 'easily' through love play (hand petting, cunnilingus, vibrator stimulation), even though many of them clearly think that they ought to do so a lot faster.

Climaxing through intercourse

In contrast, only 66 per cent of women said that they could climax easily through intercourse. And the majority of those needed additional stimulation of the clitoris in order to do it, as you've just seen.

Masturbation

'Do-it-yourself' sex is much more common in females than many people imagine. Most adult women say that they have masturbated at some time. And in answer to the question 'Do you masturbate today?' 70 per cent said 'yes' while 30 per cent said 'no'.

Masturbation with a partner

An interesting trend has emerged here. Of women who masturbate, 57 per cent say they do it *in front of their partners.*

Self-pleasuring in front of a partner has been very much encouraged in recent years by sex therapists writing in the media, since they claim (rightly, in our view) that it shows the man precisely what kind of stimulation the woman needs.

It's also a very strong turn-on to many males!

Ability to climax at will

More than two-thirds of all women (68 per cent, in fact) said that they *cannot* climax whenever they want to. Furthermore, 54 per cent of females say that they are *worried* by the fact that they think they take too long in coming. These findings have considerable implications.

Sexual intercourse climaxes *versus* love play ones

A quite remarkable feature of our survey is that most women (61 per cent) prefer the orgasms which they get through love play to the ones they get through intercourse! Only 33 per cent prefer 'intercourse orgasms'.

This is in sharp contrast with men, most of whom prefer the orgasms they have during sexual intercourse to those of love play. We suggest that our unprecedented finding underlines the great importance of clitoris stimulation for women – something of which male readers should take careful note!

Simultaneous orgasms

One of the big lies about female orgasm is that it's supposed to take place *at exactly the same time as the male has his*.

Our survey shows that this is nonsense. Only 2 per cent of the women we surveyed reported that they 'always' synchronised their climax with their partner's. As you can see from Figure 1, the biggest group of women say that they 'sometimes' come at the same time as their men. For a fifth of all couples, orgasms is *never* simultaneous.

Do women *fake* orgasm?

Yes, they most certainly do. Our results show that six out of ten women (60.5 per cent) say they have faked orgasm at some time.

Letters which women wrote to us, along with the survey form, showed that they often faked because they knew they

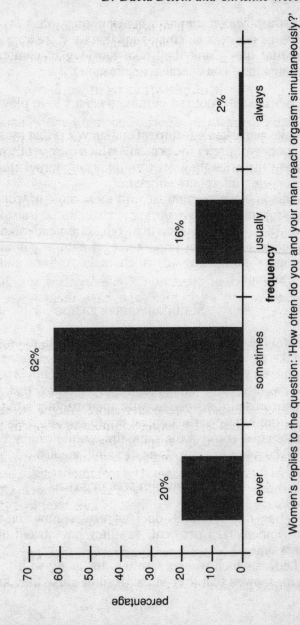

Fig. 1 Simultaneous orgasm graph

Women's replies to the question: 'How often do you and your man reach orgasm simultaneously?'

weren't going to reach an orgasm that night – and wanted to keep the man happy. Astonishingly, we also found that a lot of today's *males* are faking; see the latter part of this survey.

Multiple orgasms in women

Multiple orgasm is clearly becoming more common, as women become more liberated and (we hope) men acquire more skills. In Kinsey's day – back in the 1950s – only 14 per cent of ladies said that they could climax more than once in a session.

We found that 57 per cent of our respondents said they could 'usually' do it.

Obviously, the percentage of women who have had any multiple orgasms at all would be higher; but, alas, we did not ask that question . . .

While on the subject of multiple orgasms, we should add that there are some men who have them – see Chapter Eleven.

How many climaxes do multiple-orgasmic women have in a session?

Most female respondents seem to be happy if they have two or three, though some prefer more. When we asked the question 'What is the largest number of orgasms you have ever had?' the average response was 5.1.

However, for some multiply-orgasmic women, the most they had ever had was two. The maximum figure per session was thirty, which was claimed by several women. One or two respondents with very high totals indicated that these had been obtained mainly by masturbation.

How many orgasms do women have per week?

It's important to remember that many women – particularly

those who are not currently in a relationship – have no orgasms in a week. In contrast, there are ladies – like those mentioned above – who can tot up thirty at a single session .

So averages are fairly meaningless. But for what it is worth, the average in our survey was approximately five orgasms per week.

We noticed the following points:

* older women tended to have more orgasms than younger ones if they were in a regular relationship;
* poorer women seem to be having rather more orgasms than better-off ones. We have had many letters from executive career-women who bemoaned the fact that they simply had no time for sex. In contrast, we suspect that unemployment is having the bizarre 'side-effect' of giving some working-class couples more time to enjoy their sex lives together.

What sex position gives women the best orgasm?

Our respondents 'voted' as follows, in order of preference:

* woman on top;
* missionary;
* doggie-fashion.

Curiously, very few women mentioned the 'CAT' position, which was first suggested in the early 1990s as a way of helping the female reach a climax during coitus.

Clearly, it is not as well known as it should be. We deal with this position – and with others which may make orgasm easier – in Chapter Nine.

Are women more orgasmic at certain times of the month?

Some are, some aren't. Perhaps not surprisingly, we found that in respondents over the age of fifty, there was no difference in orgasmic capacity on any particular date. But among the under fifties, just over half (56 per cent) felt that they were more likely to come at certain times of the month. Which times? Please see Chapter Four . . .

What is women's attitude to orgasms?

It's easy to assume that climaxes are as vital to women as they are to most men, but our survey does not bear this out.

Only 12 per cent of women told us that they regarded orgasms as 'essential' to them. And only 33 per cent said they agreed with the statement 'It's better if you have them'. About half of all women thought that they were 'not necessary'!

These results may seem extraordinary – especially to males – but they are in fact very much in line with the recent findings of the British Wellcome survey, which reported that more men than women think orgasm is essential to females (37 per cent *versus* 29 per cent).

Although climaxes aren't the essence of life to ALL women, our next two questions do reveal that the lack of them is immensely frustrating to many females.

Do women often nearly get there – but not quite?

Absolutely. 55 per cent of our female respondents said that this applied to them. Many added notes to say how irritating and frustrating it is to be 'just on the brink', and then find yourself unable to quite get there.

We hope men will learn from this finding! We also hope that women will benefit from the techniques described in this book for getting over that brink.

Do women lie awake frustrated because they haven't had an orgasm?

Very definitely! No less than 57 per cent of our respondents said that they had laid awake 'desperately frustrated after a lover has fallen asleep'. Not surprisingly, a lot of them resolved this situation by masturbating – quietly!

Do women always know whether they've had an orgasm or not?

As a matter of fact, they don't (quite unlike men, who are very rarely in any serious doubt).

We found that 42 per cent of females said that they sometimes don't know whether they've come or not. So if *you* ever feel embarrassed by the fact that sometimes you don't know whether you've climaxed, please take heart: you are not alone.

PART TWO: MALES

We didn't ask as many questions of men, but the answers we got are pretty interesting. Here are the main results:

First orgasm

In males, this most commonly occurred at the age of thirteen, but the 'spread' was from eleven to sixteen.

First petting

The most common age was fifteen. This seems to have been mostly what is often politely described as hand petting – in other words stroking each other's genitals; few males report any experience of oral petting (i.e., fellatio or cunnilingus) before the age of seventeen.

First sexual intercourse

In our survey, the commonest age was seventeen but, worryingly, 35 per cent of males said that they'd lost their virginity under the age of sixteen, mostly (68 per cent) with no contraception. We most definitely do not recommend this kind of unprotected orgasm! In fact, we do not recommend under age sex at all.

Was the first experience of sexual intercourse desperately rushed?

50.1 per cent of males said 'yes'. The importance of this question lies in the fact that for many years, sex experts have tended to say that it is early *rushed* sexual experience which is the cause of premature ejaculation ('hair-trigger trouble') in adult life. Read on!

Premature ejaculation

No less than 10.8 per cent of the men in our survey said that nowadays they *always* come too soon. Furthermore, a further 60 per cent said that they 'sometimes' climax too soon.

It's a cause of real concern that the majority of males have difficulty in controlling their climaxes. And it's a tragedy that at least one in ten of the male population seem to be premature ejaculators. *You will find helpful advice on how to delay your climax in this book*.

Was there any relationship between RUSHED early sexual experience and being a premature ejaculator in adulthood? (You'll remember from the previous section that many experts think that rushed teenage experiences *cause* premature ejaculation.) Well, we did indeed find that 'early rushers' were more likely to be premature ejaculators nowadays: 18 per cent of these early rushers now have 'PE'

– as opposed to only 6 per cent of 'non-rushers'.

On the other hand, about a quarter of today's premature ejaculators did *not* have a rushed first experience, so that clearly wasn't the cause of the problem in their case. Furthermore, you have to bear in mind that premature ejaculation could be the *cause* of first sex being 'desperately rushed'.

How long does sexual intercourse last today?

According to our male respondents, the average is twenty-one minutes and fifteen seconds. Whether their female partners would agree or not is another matter – next time we'll ask them!

But almost a fifth of men (19.5 per cent) said that for them, intercourse lasted *less than five minutes*. This was a very honest admission, and it certainly does bear out the frequent complaint of females that 'some men do it far too fast'.

Do men feel they are getting enough love play from women?

We asked males whether their partners gave them enough love play. Surprisingly, well over a third of men (36 per cent) said 'No'. We use the word 'surprisingly' because it is traditionally said that it's *women* who want lots of love play, while men don't! But it seems from our figures that many men would relish more kissing and cuddling from their partners. And the letters we received from them make clear that, in particular, they would appreciate more hand-stimulation and fellatio.

Do men say that they and their partners have simultaneous climaxes?

Slightly to our surprise, the men gave almost identical

answers to the women. They confirm that only a tiny percentage of couples (2 per cent) *always* reach orgasm at the same time.

Furthermore, only one in six 'usually' reach it simultaneously. But about six out of ten men (and women) say that they 'sometimes' achieve this happy fusion.

Do men prefer orgasms from love play, or orgasms from intercourse?

As you'll have seen from the earlier part of the survey, our very striking finding is that a majority of *women* prefer the climaxes which they get from love play.

In sharp contrast, the great majority of males (73 per cent) prefer having an orgasm from intercourse. Only 27 per cent prefer the climaxes they get from love play (the corresponding figure for women is 61 per cent). This dramatically differing result seems to us to emphasise the extraordinary importance which the male mind attaches to having one's orgasm *inside a woman*.

How many orgasms do males have per week?

As we point out in Chapter Eleven, men tend to lie in the most disgraceful way about how often they can do it – particularly if a woman is present! (Some men filled in their forms with a partner there . . .) But for what it's worth, our finding is that the average male claims 4.1 orgasms per week from all sources, including intercourse, love play, masturbation and 'wet dreams'.

We would point out that we *discarded* the tiny handful of questionnaires we received from silly young men who claimed to have 100 orgasms a night – except when it was Sharon Stone's evening off . . .

PART ONE

Women's Orgasms

1

WHAT HAPPENS TO THE FEMALE BODY AT ORGASM?

The Myth • The Reality • What Actually IS an Orgasm? • The Need For Gentle Preparation • What a Woman Looks Like (and Sounds Like) During Orgasm • Breasts During Orgasm • Limbs During Orgasm • Bottom During Orgasm • Vulva and Clitoris During Orgasm • Vagina During Orgasm • Womb During Orgasm • Feelings During Orgasm • What Are the Common Ways In Which Women Reach Orgasm? • Masturbation • Vibrators • Hand Petting ('Touching Up') • Cunnilingus • Intercourse • Multiple Orgasms • Do Women Ejaculate During Orgasm? • The Female G-spot and Orgasm • Orgasm and Conception • Orgasm and Pregnancy • Orgasm and the Mature Woman • How Often Do Women Have Orgasms? • The New 'Orgasm Nose Spray'

THE MYTH

There is a glorious myth about female orgasm, and it is heavily encouraged by the romantic fiction which women traditionally read – and indeed by the erotic books, specially written for a female readership, which have become so widespread since the early 1990s (not to mention by the rude material that so many men read – see Chapter 11!).

The myth is that female orgasm is always effortless and heart-stoppingly wonderful – a cataclysmic experience of quite enormous pleasure which a woman can enjoy *at will*, and repeat again and again.

Here's the sort of thing we mean:

‘A cruel smile played across Don Fernando's rakishly handsome features as he strapped Rosemary's slim, girlish wrists and ankles to the four posts of the royal bed. She shivered with a delicious mixture of desire and fear as he ripped her flimsy negligée away from her generous breasts, and then gazed with harsh masculine lust at her naked groin.

Next, he pulled off his belt and breeches and flung his hard, sun-burnt body onto her. As he took her precious virginity away, she found to her astonishment that her heart seemed to be filled with joy. Oh, if this could only go on for ever . . .

Moments later, a strange sensation began to arise inside her. It started like a far-away whispering in her loins; then it became an insistent flutter in her womb – which progressed to a tremendous pulsation that seemed to overwhelm her mind and body with glorious waves of ecstasy.

Finally, an incandescent rocket burst inside her mind, and she screamed out with a wild passion that was almost pain – screamed so loudly, in fact, that the *cicadas* in the garden outside the royal palace ceased their song for a while . . .

When she regained consciousness, Don Fernando was gazing at her with a much more tender expression on his tanned face. Taking her in his strong arms, he kissed her gently, then began making love to her once more.

And again and again, the same wonderful sensation of exquisite delight swept over her – always occurring just at the very moment when he too reached the peak of his pleasure. And each time that she experienced this marvellous release, she could not help noticing that a dewy liquid spurted forth from her body, as if to demonstrate her joy at being possessed by this astonishing, savage, magnificent male.

Afterwards, he served her a glass of the finest, nut-brown, sweet sherry . . .*'*

Well, this gloriously barmy-yet-erotic story (at least, we *hope* you found it erotic!) embodies various bits of widely believed nonsense about female orgasm. They are:

* that a climax is easy to achieve;
* that it happens very quickly;
* that it should occur without any need for gentle preparation, romancing, cuddling or love play;
* that it requires no special attention to the woman's clitoris – just straight, no-nonsense sexual intercourse;
* that even when a woman is busy losing her virginity, she should not fail to orgasm;
* that the woman's climax should happen *simultaneously* with her partner's on all occasions;
* that female orgasm ought to be accompanied by a sudden 'spurting' of some exotic, deliciously scented liquid from the woman's most intimate parts;
* most importantly, that she should be able to climax again and again and again!

THE REALITY

Now although female orgasm can be a wonderful experience, the truth about it is very different from the above. So let's look at all those points one by one:

- a climax is *not* easy to achieve for most women – specially when they are young – as you'll find in this book, the majority of ladies *learn* over a period of years to achieve very easy orgasm with a loving partner;
- orgasm doesn't usually happen in a matter of moments. Unlike males (some of whom can 'come' within thirty seconds or so) females mostly take quite a long time to warm up. Yes, there *are* women – like the famous actress mentioned in the Introduction to this book – who can climax in four minutes flat, if the atmosphere is right. The great Dr Kinsey claimed that he had found some ladies 'who respond faster than any male'. **Most females require lots of time**. From a 'standing start', the average is about sixteen minutes!
- orgasm is most unlikely to happen *unless* the woman has been carefully and tenderly wooed, cuddled, caressed, kissed and generally made to feel wanted;
- in the great majority of cases, a man is *not* going to make a woman orgasm *unless* he pays a good deal of attention to her clitoris;
- most women do *not* have an orgasm when they lose their virginity (though amazingly some *do* – perhaps because of the excitement of the occasion – see Chapter Three);
- in the vast majority of acts of sexual intercourse, simultaneous orgasm does *not* occur – if it happens to you, you're lucky, but only 2 per cent of women told us that this 'always' occurred for them;
- with regard to the 'spurting of dewy fluid' at orgasm, so beloved of the authors of erotic novels, this happens in

only a tiny minority of women (but we have to admit that it does happen – see the section of this book about the female G-spot);
• about 'doing it again and again' – actually, our survey suggests that an ever-increasing number of women are genuinely capable of multiple orgasms, and that this ability is particularly high in the *older* age groups – but for many females, it's normal just to have *one* orgasm in a session.

So, a more accurate account of an average female's orgasmic encounter might read something like this:

⁶Valerie always liked meeting up with Sean when she visited his town on business, because he was good fun and understood what she wanted in bed. So that night she was very pleased to invite him to dinner – and back to her hotel room afterwards.

In the room, they spent some time kissing and cuddling, and Sean pleased her by telling her what good shape she was looking in. Eventually, she went off to the bathroom and stripped off, while he hopped into the bed and warmed it up!

Once they were snuggled up together, he spent about twenty minutes kissing and stroking her all over, not neglecting to murmur romantic things in her ear, until eventually he turned his attention to her now-dripping vulva.

He began by caressing it with his fingers, and then eventually applied his tongue to it, cleverly using its tip to excite her clitoris, and moving his lips around exactly as she directed.

After they'd been in bed about an hour, she had a *very* satisfying climax. Knowing that she had a long day tomorrow, she decided that enough was enough and asked him to go ahead and "have" her. This he did with great pleasure!

As he fell happily asleep in her arms, she toyed

briefly with the idea of "touching herself up" and giving herself a second orgasm. But then, realising that it was long past midnight, she decided to roll over towards Sean, tuck herself up comfortably against his bottom, and drift off into slumber . . . **'**

WHAT ACTUALLY *IS* AN ORGASM?

Now what actually *is* an orgasm?

The answer may seem obvious, but you'll find that it's not quite that simple! You see, in our survey, no less than 42 per cent of women said that there were times when they weren't sure whether they'd had one or not. (Men virtually *never* have such doubts about themselves . . .)

Female orgasm isn't easy to define. Dr Kinsey tried. He said 'There is a build-up of neuro-muscular tensions, which may culminate at a peak.'

Quite so. Trying to be a little bit more specific, we'd say that what happens during a female climax is something like this:

* *provided* that she is in a receptive mood (because if she isn't, it's just not going to work!), sexual stimulation of her vagina and or clitoris will start sending powerful erotic messages up through her spinal cord to her brain;
* as a result of these messages, she will become more and more excited; her breathing will gradually get faster and faster, and her heart will pound; the muscles of her body and face will get tenser and tenser;
* eventually there will come a moment of absolutely *tremendous* tension – like the moment before a balloon bursts;
* suddenly that tension will be released, as a convulsion shakes the woman's entire frame; this discharge of

nervous energy is something like The World's Biggest Sneeze – except that it's the most pleasurable thing in the world;

- as the tension ebbs away, the woman will usually feel what's often described as 'a blessed sense of relief';
- however . . . as we'll see shortly, one of the main differences between male and female orgasm is that a woman may well be ready and eager to go through the whole thing again within a matter of a minute or two!

In a moment, we'll have a look at how an orgasm affects all the various bits of the female body. But first a word of advice . . .

THE NEED FOR GENTLE PREPARATION

If you're a man, we beg you to appreciate that *women are not machines.*

Men are not machines, either – but most of them can reach orgasm very, very easily. Women – as our survey clearly shows – have much, much more difficulty in reaching climaxes.

We sometimes get letters from male readers who say idiotic things like, 'I am just writing to let you know that my wife's clitoris does not work.' What such gentlemen do not realise is that the clitoris isn't a sort of automatic button, like the thing you push when you want a slot-machine to give you a bar of chocolate.

Stimulating it will *help* bring a woman to a climax – but *only* if the atmosphere is right, and if she has been gently and sexily prepared for it.

Unfortunately, a high proportion of men still haven't got this message. We could paper a wall with the letters we receive each week which contain sentences along the lines of

'My man doesn't give me anything like enough time'.

So, gents, we suggest that you follow these guidelines:

* never rush a woman;
* always kiss, cuddle and caress her before you even *start* on any kind of serious sexual approach;
* unless she tells you otherwise, assume that she would prefer a good *half-hour* of love play before intercourse starts;
* be guided *by her* as to the sort of love play she wants;
* don't make a wild grab for the clitoris and think that doing that will make everything OK;
* when you finally do get to the area of the clitoris, be gentle with it, and stroke its sides, rather than pressing directly on its tip – see Chapter Ten;
* don't assume that clitoral stimulation *alone* will make her orgasm – many women need *two* kinds of stimulation as we'll see in a moment;
* at all costs, don't keep asking her if she's 'nearly there yet'!

WHAT A WOMAN LOOKS LIKE (AND SOUNDS LIKE) DURING ORGASM

As we've seen, many women are sometimes uncertain whether or not they've reached an orgasm.

So it's scarcely surprising that a lot of *men* have difficulty in telling whether their partners have come! This leads to all sorts of confusion – especially if the male wrongly decides that the female has climaxed, stops stimulating her, and goes off to sleep (a common occurrence . . .).

Well, what are the signs which indicate that a woman is climaxing? Let's list them:

* as we've said above, her breathing gets faster and faster – and indeed louder and louder – till she's virtually gasping for air, just before the moment of orgasm;

- her eyes become 'glazed', and are no longer focusing;
- her muscles – including her facial muscles – become tighter and tighter, so that just before she actually comes, her expression is so intense that it could easily be mistaken for one of great pain;
- she may call out various things repeatedly (yes, just like the scene in *When Harry Met Sally* . . .) as she approaches her climax; very commonly, women cry out repetitive, simple, but highly charged phrases. Examples are:

'I love you/I love you/I LOVE YOU . . .'
'Now/Now/Now/NOW . . .'
'Oh yes/Oh yes/OH YES . . .'
'Fuck me/Fuck me/FUCK ME . . .'
'Oh God/Oh God/Oh God/OH GOD . . .'

We're sorry if the last phrase offends any readers, but it is a fact that women do often shout out religious phrases in moments of extreme passion.

- as everything reaches a peak, she will usually let rip *with a wild cry*. This is about the surest indication that orgasm has really occurred unless, of course, she is faking! This is pretty common, as you can see from our survey. We found that six out of ten women have done it at some time.

   The cry varies in intensity from woman to woman – and it also varies a great deal from one occasion to another. There are times when it may be nothing more than a muffled squeak – especially as most females do have the capacity to 'keep it quiet' when other people might overhear them.

   But on other occasions – particularly when a passionate woman is extremely tensed up – the cry may well be a full-blooded scream that could be heard half a block away.

   We know of an American woman who had tremendous sex during an episode of great stress in her life. Her mighty orgasm was, to say the least, an enormous relief to her. And although she was lying face-down on her pillow in her third-floor apartment, she still produced a colossal shriek which frightened the mailman who was standing on the sidewalk; he promptly dropped her letters. But *she* felt a great deal better and calmer, and was able to face a very difficult interview with her boss, which was scheduled for later that day. (There is no question that a good orgasm can greatly reduce stress levels!)

- other external changes take place in the female body at orgasm – for instance, a pinkish rash on the chest (in fair-skinned women only), curling-up of the toes, and twitching of the anus. But in all honesty, these are *not* very easy for a partner to spot! So our advice to males is to rely mainly on 'the cry' as a guide to whether your partner is reaching the Big O.

Most women readers of this book will not have seen a female climax, unless of course they have dabbled in lesbianism. Alas, you cannot *watch* yourself come – because your eyes will close at the critical moment. So if you are very interested in seeing what your own orgasm is like, there is no harm in following a recent trend and using your home camcorder to video yourself during a climax. You may be surprised by what you see, but many women find it a considerable turn-on.

Do, however, make sure that you wipe the tape afterwards. This is not the sort of thing that you would want to get into the wrong hands – especially those of your children.

BREASTS DURING ORGASM

Now let's see how the various parts of a woman's body behave during orgasm – starting with her breasts.

There are two main changes which happen as a result of sexual excitement:

- nipple erection;
- enlargement of the breasts.

You can see the whole process in Figure 1.1. The *first* picture shows the 'unaroused' human breast. The *second* one shows what happens when sexual excitement starts: the woman's nipple begins to stick out prominently.

Incidentally, this is a tremendous turn-on for many males! We recently read an account by a man of how he and his friends passed through puberty; he mentioned specifically that when these lads were in a high state of sexual excitement the mere mention of the phrase 'sticky-out nipples' was enough to tip them over into orgasm . . .

The *third* drawing shows what the breast is like in the final stage before orgasm. You'll see that it has enlarged in size – again, a great turn-on to men – and the brown or pink area round the nipple (the 'areola') has swollen up so that the nipple itself isn't quite so prominent.

At this stage, just before the actual climax, the veins on the breasts (blue in fair-skinned women, dark in brown-skinned or black-skinned ones) may stand out very prominently. Once again, this is a turn-on signal to a lot of males.

Then comes the moment of orgasm itself, and the swelling at the front of the breasts instantly starts to go down a little – so that the nipple is once again sticking out, as in the *fourth* drawing.

Unless the woman promptly has another climax, the size of her breasts will gradually go down a little over the next ten minutes or so, while the 'sex flush' on the skin of her breasts will slowly disappear.

Note: If you have had several babies, the changes in your breasts may not be quite as dramatic as those we've described. But the pleasure which you get from your breasts should be just the same.

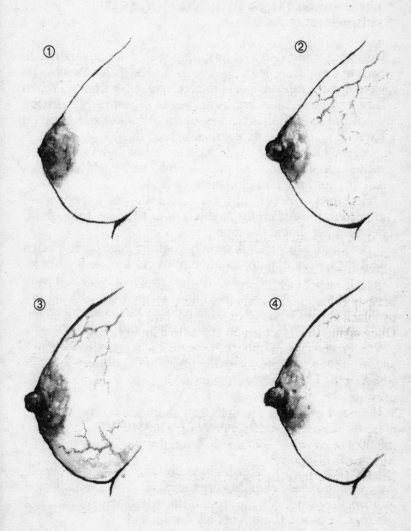

Fig. 1.1

LIMBS DURING ORGASM

During a climax, it's almost impossible for a woman to control her arms, legs, fingers and toes. (This is why we were considerably alarmed to receive a letter from a French lady who sometimes brings herself to orgasm while driving down the long, dull stretches of the A6 *autoroute* between Paris and Dijon. We do *not* recommend this.)

As she hits the Big O, the muscles of her limbs will tighten with surprising force, so that she may well curl her fingers and dig her nails into her partner's flesh.

Her toes will curl up, too – and this is a very good indication of orgasm for anybody who happens to be down between her feet at the time!

Her thigh muscles will usually contract vigorously – often as if they were making an attempt to get a male further in. And, perhaps most importantly, the various muscles around the tops of her legs and her hips will, as a rule, thrust her pelvis violently forward in repeated surges. It's a curious but welcome characteristic of both female and male sexuality that as orgasm approaches we seem to be automatically programmed to start this instinctive and intensely erotic thrusting of the hips.

BOTTOM DURING ORGASM

If you're a little squeamish about bottoms – as many people are – then please skip this brief section! As we've indicated above, the opening of the rectum (the anus) actually twitches in many women, though not all, during a climax.

These involuntary twitches happen simultaneously with the surging contractions which she feels in the region of her vagina. But just *before* the orgasm, many women voluntarily contract their rectal muscles, because (according to Masters and Johnson, who were in a position to know about these things) they have found that this pleasurable contraction of the bottom helps drive them onwards to climax.

If this works for you, then by all means use it.

VULVA AND CLITORIS DURING ORGASM

The vulva, in case you're in any doubt (many people are) is the opening which leads to the vagina – in other words, the visible part of the female sex organ.

What happens to it as a woman approaches orgasm? These are the main changes:

* as she grows more excited, quite a lot of natural lubricating fluid ('love juice') appears from inside the vulva. This is actually produced by the walls of her vagina, and it makes sex a great deal easier and nicer – without its lubricating effect, there would be discomfort and pain. In order to help achieve orgasm, we recommend that you transfer some of it to the lady's clitoris, which can easily get dry and sore.
* her 'lips' (labia) swell a little, as the woman's gradually increasing sexual excitement makes blood flow into them. They also part a little as though getting ready to welcome her partner's penis.
* just before the orgasm occurs, her *inner* lips change colour quite strikingly to a bright red, or sometimes deep burgundy, colour; if she is actually having intercourse, the swollen lips will now be gently 'gripping' her man's organ.

What about the clitoris itself? As the woman starts to get excited, it swells up a little, just as a male's penis does, but to nothing like the same size – the visible part of it never gets any bigger than a raisin. But it becomes intensely sensitive to sexual stimulation, and for the few seconds before orgasm occurs it may seem to the woman as though it is the centre of her whole being.

Be warned: when the climax actually happens the clitoris can quite often become immensely tender for a minute or two (much as the penis does after orgasm in many men). A skilled lover should be on the look-out for this post-orgasm phenomenon and – if asked to do so – *stop* rubbing the *cli-cli* at once!

VAGINA DURING ORGASM

Now what about the woman's vagina – that tender, pink tunnel whose only function is to enclose the penis and give both partners great pleasure? (People think that the vagina has a function in childbirth, but that isn't true.)

Well, as we've seen above it is now known that the cushiony *walls* of the vagina produce that pleasant lubricating fluid which flows out whenever a woman starts to get sexually excited. This can happen within ten seconds of thinking about a lover.

What next? As her arousal increases, a woman's vagina starts becoming *longer* and more *roomy*. Have a look at the little arrows in Figure 1.2 and you'll see what we mean.

She is quite unaware of this change, but it does in fact make it possible for a female to have intercourse with almost *any* male, regardless of how big his organ is or how small she thinks she is.

As orgasm approaches, the outer couple of inches of her vagina swell up a little. The purpose of this is to ensure a nice, snug fit round her partner's shaft. Those outer couple of inches constitute what we've christened the 'S-zone.' S stands for 'stretch', and the point is that in the run-up to orgasm, many ladies find that gentle *stretching* of this ring is

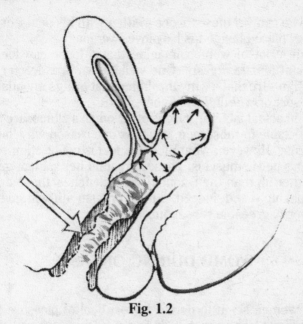

Fig. 1.2

not only a terrific turn-on, but also helps them along the road
to climax. The 'S-zone' is indicated by the white arrow above.

Indeed as we'll see later in this chapter, a combination of
stretching this 'S-zone' (see Fig 1.2), *together* with
stimulation of the clitoris is probably the best of all ways of
ensuring that an orgasm is achieved.

Now Masters and Johnson (the great American experts on
sex) have always said that at the moment of climax, the area
of the S-zone starts to *throb* rhythmically, as shown in Figure
1.1. They base this claim on the pioneering experiments they
did in the laboratory, which involved putting miniature
cameras inside women's vaginas while they climaxed . . .

Certainly, a woman *does* feel a powerful orgasmic
throbbing in the region of her vagina. These throbs happen
every four-fifths of a second – just like the pulse of a man's
climax. But a curious thing is that we have not yet found a

man who can *feel* these throbs – either with his penis, or with a finger placed inside his lady-love's vagina.

Quite a lot of women imagine that a lover can feel the throbs of female orgasm. One well-known broadcaster said to us: 'I'm sure that it's my throbbing that brings my husband off. It sort of *milks* him as I come.'

But in actual fact, the surges of a woman's climax are quite undetectable to most men, which is one reason why 'faking' is so easy. However, what men *can* feel is contraction of the woman's pelvic muscles. These surround her vagina, quite a bit higher up than the S-zone. If she 'clenches' these during love-making – and, indeed, during orgasm – it will give her man very agreeable sensations indeed.

WOMB DURING ORGASM

Many women seem to derive a great deal of pleasure from contractions of the womb during orgasm – which is one reason why you should think carefully before agreeing to have a hysterectomy (removal of the womb). If your gynaecologist suggests that you should have a hysterectomy, you should question him/her closely about the possible effect on your orgasms. There is some evidence that there *may* be less interference with orgasmic contractions if the surgeon doesn't remove your cervix (the lowest part – or 'neck' – of your womb).

Thanks to the famous Masters and Johnson, we now know that what happens to the womb during sex is this. As soon as a woman starts getting excited her womb *lifts upwards* – thus making extra room in her vagina for the penis. When she actually comes, her womb goes into a series of contractions. These contractions give her very nice 'pulsing' feelings, deep in her body.

It's not yet clear whether the contractions help her to

conceive or not – see 'Orgasms and Conception', later in this chapter.

FEELINGS DURING ORGASM

So all these powerful contractions in her pelvic region, together with the erotic sensations sweeping up from the area of her clitoris and the good feelings in her breasts and nipples, all combine to give a woman the most overwhelming experience of great pleasure – and great relief from sexual tension – as orgasm happens.

It's a truly shattering event – and the extraordinary fact is that so many females can summon up the energy to do the whole thing again in a few minutes, as we'll see in the section on multiple orgasms later in this chapter (see page 49).

As to what women *think* during climaxes, we'll deal with that in Chapter Five.

WHAT ARE THE COMMON WAYS IN WHICH WOMEN REACH ORGASM?

Until quite recent years, the 'polite' view was that if women reached orgasm at all (and remember, it was a scarcely mentionable subject!) then they would do so through sexual intercourse with their husbands – and *definitely* not in any other way.

As late as the mid-1970s, one of us suggested in a women's magazine that many adult females regularly 'touched themselves up'. This caused a deluge of protest letters from people who declared that it was 'unthinkable' that ladies could behave in this way. Slightly hilariously, all of them were from men . . .

We have found that today's women reach their climaxes in all sorts of ways: masturbation, vibrator use, hand-petting ('frigging'), cunnilingus, and, of course, intercourse. And a few climaxes are reached in dreams – very much like the 'wet dreams' that men have.

Our female respondents told us that the *principal* ways in which they reach orgasm these days are as follows:

Masturbation	12 %
Love play	4 %
Oral sex	1 %
A mixture of love play and intercourse	50 %
Intercourse with added clitoral stimulation needed	20 %
Intercourse with no added stimulation	13 %

Although we did not ask specifically about vibrator use in this question, we enquired about it under a separate heading, and found that about 40 per cent of female respondents had tried one, either during masturbation or love play.

So let's look now at how the various methods can help a woman reach her climax.

Note: Through an omission on our part, we did not ask about climaxes through *lesbian* activity. But these are probably less common than many people – particularly highly sexed males! – imagine. For instance, in the recent British Wellcome survey only 0.4 per cent of women reported lesbian activity in the last year.

Similarly, in the 1995 University of Chicago study, only 1.3 per cent of American women reported having sex with another female in the previous twelve months. And the recent French ACSF survey found that only 0.3 per cent of French women admitted to bedding another *femme* in the last year. How very different from what goes on in French literature!

Admittedly, gay groups have indignantly claimed – probably with justification – that these figures are serious under-estimates, thanks to the fact that women are wary of 'confessing' to Sapphic sex.

Nevertheless, it does appear to us that lesbian orgasms are fairly uncommon, compared with other types. (This does not alter the fact that many women admit to *fantasising* about them.)

MASTURBATION

Very much in line with other surveys which have been carried out in the USA, Britain, Australia and elsewhere in recent years, we find that about 93 per cent of our female respondents have masturbated to orgasm at some time or another.

Seven out of ten of our respondents tell us that they are doing it *now*. And you may be surprised to learn that that includes a very high proportion of married women. This doesn't by any means imply that these ladies are being in some way 'unfaithful' to their husbands when they touch themselves up.

You see, we specifically asked women to tell us if they 'frigged' in front of their partners. And six out of ten of those who currently masturbate do it with their menfolk there.

The main reasons for this trend appear to be these:

• many males – particularly younger and more liberated ones – find this greatly exciting (which is why men's magazines so frequently feature female masturbatory activity);
• some women also find it a turn-on;

- it shows the male partner *exactly* what sort of techniques he should be using during 'finger play';
- if the woman isn't getting anywhere with what her man's doing to her, she may well decide to take things into her own hands (and more power to her elbow, we say).

Additionally, it's worth noting that a lot of women now tell us that they frig themselves *during intercourse*. This is very reasonable, since – as we repeatedly stress in this book – intercourse alone is often quite insufficient to help a woman reach a climax.

In these cases, the man may or may not be aware that his partner is 'rubbing herself up' during love-making. There are certain positions (particularly rear-entry ones) where it would not be easy for him to tell – especially in the dark.

What techniques of do-it-yourself sex do today's women use to bring themselves to a climax? The commonest appears to be simple rubbing with either one finger tip or two, *just alongside the clitoris*.

Not until the woman is fairly heavily aroused does she tend to move her fingers on to the body of the clitoris itself, often as orgasm approaches.

Male readers of this book would do well to study this technique, since for obvious reasons it is by far the most important basic manoeuvre to learn if you want to 'bring off' your partner. It is shown clearly in Figure 1.3. If you're a man, take special care *not* to move on to the head of the clitoris unless your lady asks you to do so!

VIBRATORS

One of the big changes in sexual behaviour in Western countries in recent years has been the advent of vibrators. Many women now use these to achieve orgasm – either

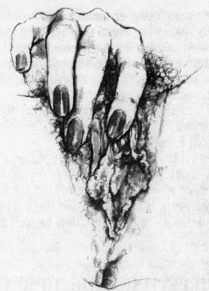

Fig. 1.3

during love play, or by themselves. We found that approximately four out of ten of our sample of adult females had tried vibrators at some time, though not all had persisted with them.

Vibrators are in fact very effective at stimulating female orgasm, simply because they move very fast, and do not get tired! When you bear in mind that human fingers (both male and female) *do* get tired, you can see why vibrators are so popular.

We find that it is the more mature groups of women who use them most – and of course it is in the older age groups that people tend to have lost their partners, and therefore go in more for solo sex.

Also, in the case of older couples it's quite often the case that the man may be affected by conditions such as arthritis of the hands, and so may be only too glad to be able to make his partner come with one of these little electrical devices.

How are they used in order to promote orgasm? There are all sorts of ways, but we'll confine ourselves to explaining how the commonest type of vibrator is employed.

This type is often described as 'penis-shaped', but some women prefer to call it 'vagina-shaped'. However, though it can indeed be put right into the vagina, exactly like a male organ, the normal thing is to apply it to the area of the clitoris, just as in Figure 1.4.

Please note that it should usually be applied alongside the *cli-cli* (as the French call it), rather than on top of it.

Some women do also like to use the vibrator to stretch the S-zone (i.e., by having it put just inside the vagina). But they will usually require clitoral stimulation as well if they are to reach orgasm.

HAND-PETTING ('TOUCHING UP')

As we've seen, this is a very common way of reaching orgasm, and knowledge of how to do it to a woman is essential for any man who wants to help his partner to climax. There are all sorts of possible techniques, but they fall mainly into two groups:

- clitoral;
- vaginal.

Clitoral techniques

As we've seen, some sort of stimulation of the clitoris is usually essential if the woman is to reach the Big O.

What ladies generally prefer is a finger technique *which mimics the way in which they stimulate their own clitorises*. If you look back a few pages to the section on masturbation,

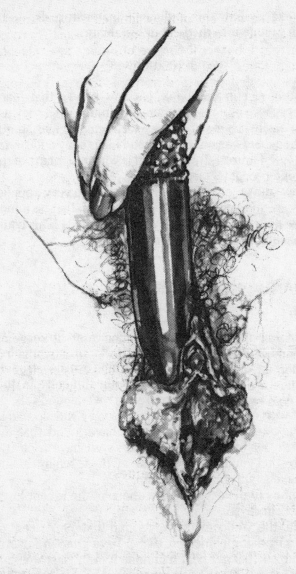

Fig. 1.4

you'll see exactly how this is done. A man can really do no better than imitate it to the best of his ability . . .

Vaginal techniques

As we said earlier in this book, it's now known that many women need both clitoral *and* vaginal stimulation if they are to orgasm easily. There are many different vaginal stimulation methods, but basically it's a good idea to try and *stretch the S-zone* (see Figure 1.2), since that is where so many of the female 'erotic receptors' are located.

In-and-out movements of the fingers are also very popular, but do be careful to carry these out gently, so that you don't damage the delicate tissues with your finger nails. This could put your partner right off orgasm that night.

CUNNILINGUS

This means kissing or tonguing the female sex organs. It's also known as 'Frenching'. Cunnilingus is a highly effective way of bringing a woman to orgasm, and we do strongly recommend it to people who are having difficulty in this direction. Although older and more narrow-minded folk do still view it with suspicion, cunnilingus is very widespread in all Western countries these days. We have found that the great majority of women we have surveyed have tried it – particularly the young – and most of those enjoy it and regard it as a useful route to orgasm.

Our findings fit in very well with those of the recent huge national sex surveys.

In Britain, the Wellcome survey found that 69 per cent of women (a surprising coincidence . . .) have gone in for oral sex, and indeed 19.9 per cent had done it in the last week.

Similarly, the 1995 USA survey by the University of

Chicago finds that almost *one in five* American women did it during their last sexual encounter. The third of the recent great national sex surveys (the French one) did not ask about cunnilingus – perhaps on the assumption that *all* French women do it?

In our own study, we found that only 1 per cent of women said that cunnilingus was their 'principal' source of orgasms. But this is perfectly reasonable, since most couples tend to employ Frenching as part of a range of activities.

Thus a highly-sexed woman might well spend an agreeable evening in which she has one climax this way, three by hand, and one during intercourse. And very often, a couple will use cunnilingus to get the female partner really worked up, and then do something else to bring her to the actual orgasm. The choice is yours.

Cunnilingus is *not* easy at first and it requires a lot of practice before your partner can become really good at bringing you to a climax.

Detailed descriptions of the various methods of cunnilingus are outside the scope of this book, but in general it's a good idea for the man to begin by using his lips and his tongue to stimulate the area *near* the woman's clitoris – and then let her guide him to the exact point (or points) where she wants pressure and friction.

Keeping things moist – either with saliva or with a purpose-designed oral sex lubricant – will increase the chances of successfully 'fetching her off'.

INTERCOURSE

As you'll have noticed if you've looked at the results of our survey, sexual intercourse is – quite naturally – the source of many orgasms for women. But sadly, it's not a very *good* way of inducing orgasm, which is why so many of our female respondents have said that they need additional stimulation during intercourse to make them come.

Why isn't it a very good way?

Well, as one of us (DD) demonstrated recently with his hands, on his TV series *The Good Sex Guide*, the problem is that the clitoris isn't really in the right place for intercourse!

Look at DD's hands in Figure 1.5. The thumb represents the penis going in, and the clitoris is represented by the dark circle drawn on the knuckle. You'll note that they don't get anywhere near each other!

During intercourse, the lady's clitoris receives *some* compression from the man's pubic bone (the hard part, lying underneath his pubic hair), but it's not very much. In short, there does seem to be a bit of a 'design fault' here . . .

This knowledge first became widespread in America about a quarter of a century ago. In an attempt to remedy the situation, quite a lot of American couples started trying to make love in such a way that the gentleman's penis hit against the lady's clitoris, before bouncing inside.

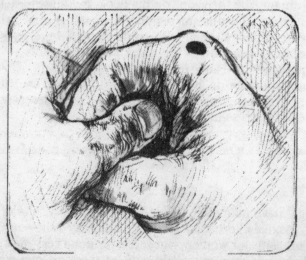

Fig. 1.5

Such a procedure is technically possible, but it's rather difficult to do repeatedly. Also, it feels rather like pole-vaulting. Another effort to solve the problem was made by the sex aid manufacturers, who came up with the invention called a 'clitoral stimulator'. This is a device which fits round the man's organ; it has a projection on the top which is supposed to rub on the woman's clitoris and help her reach orgasm. A nice idea – but not wildly successful.

During the 1990s, there has been a new approach to the problem – the 'CAT technique'. This is really a sexual position in which the man's body is specially aligned in order to give more pressure on the clitoris. We explain it fully in Chapter Nine.

But in most positions of sexual intercourse, the lady's *cli-cli* simply does not get enough stimulation to make orgasm easily achievable. So what we recommend is that, whenever possible, you should try and stimulate the clitoris *by hand* during intercourse.

This is more easy in certain positions than in others! In the standard 'face-to-face' positions, it can be almost impossible for the man to get his fingertips on to the region of his partner's clitoris – simply because the human hand doesn't bend that way.

In such circumstances, it's often a lot easier if the *woman* slips her fingers down between the two partners and rubs her own clitoris, because her hand will bend the right way to do this.

Such an arrangement will very often lead to a successful orgasm in cases where the woman was having considerable difficulty.

MULTIPLE ORGASMS

On to the subject of multiple orgasms in women. There is a relatively small number of *men* who can have multiple orgasms, but it is women who have the real ability in this field! We state confidently here that **most women have the ability to have multiple orgasms if they want to**.

Now, if you *don't* want to, and are quite happy as you are, then it really doesn't matter. But in recent years, increasing numbers of women have happily joined the ranks of the multiply orgasmic, and most of them seem to be quite pleased about it.

The ability to have multiple climaxes wasn't always widespread. Back in the good Dr Kinsey's day (the early 1950s), he reported that only *one in seven* American females could come more than once. However, ladies have become much more liberated since then, and (we believe) men have got much better at stimulating them. Also, there are such things as vibrators . . .

The results are clear. In our survey, we find that *nearly six out of ten* of our respondents say that they 'usually' have more than one climax in a session. The percentage of women who have *ever* had more than one orgasm would clearly be much higher.

Incidentally, we noted that the incidence of multiple climaxes was appreciably greater in those women who are currently in a stable relationship. Obviously, if you've settled down with a loving partner and got used to him, your chances of repeated orgasms are greater.

Perhaps you think our findings are surprising, but they are in fact broadly in line with those of recent studies in Australia and America – where the rather happily named Dr Darling and her colleague Dr Davidson have recently found virtually half of all women having multiple orgasms. Dr Davidson agrees that 'every woman is physically capable of them'.

Are there any particular characteristics which make a woman the type who can have multiple orgasms? Are they all super-sexy ladies with big breasts and permanently moist vaginas? Certainly not! We find that quite a lot of women with relatively modest sex drives can be multi-orgasmic if they so wish.

A paper published in the medical journal *Archives of Sexual Behavior* in 1991 reported how the above-mentioned Dr Darling, of Florida State University, and her colleagues tried to determine whether multiply orgasmic females had different behaviours and perceptions from singly orgasmic ones. They looked at a huge group of multiple-climaxing nurses ('multas') living in various parts of the USA, and compared them with nurses who do *not* have multiple orgasms. The only big differences they could find between the two groups were:

- the 'multas' were more likely to have examined their own clitorises;
- they were more likely to go in for oral sex;
- when masturbating, they were more likely to put their fingers inside;
- they were more likely to use thigh pressure to stimulate their own clitorises;
- they were *much* more likely to use sexual fantasies, and erotic literature and films.

How on Earth do women manage to have multiple orgasms? This a subject of some confusion to many men – because after a climax most males would be completely incapable of even having an erection, never mind another orgasm.

The answer seems to be that when a female has just climaxed, she does not 'descend' with the same rapidity that males do. For quite a while after coming, she is still quite sexually excited, and very capable of being taken up to the peak again.

A useful analogy is this. When a man climaxes, it's like going to the top of a mountain and returning to sea-level again. But when a woman climaxes, it's as if she reaches the summit, and then climbs down to rest for a bit in a mountain hut just below the peak. With sufficient encouragement, she'll gladly jog up the short path to the top again, maybe quite a few times.

How many times?

Well, it seems that two or three is about average. When asked what was the greatest number they'd achieved, the women in our survey reported a mean of just over five. But several women told us that they had recorded thirty orgasms in a session on occasions. If you are astonished by this, we can assure you that you have no reason to be so. We have incontrovertible evidence of women reaching that sort of number – and there are sporadic reports in the literature (or perhaps the cliterature) of highly sexed females clocking up much more.

However, women – very sensibly – do not seem keen to try and set up sexual records in the matter of multiple orgasms. This is just as well, because they can leave you *very* tired next day.

What can you do if you *want* to be multiply orgasmic? Well, the best thing is to have a loving partner who wants to help you and who knows what he's doing. But there is a case for learning to be a 'multa' through masturbation, perhaps with a vibrator.

Whatever way you choose, set aside plenty of time, by which we mean several hours per occasion, in a warm, comfortable setting where you will not be interrupted. Don't set yourself goals, but instead decide that a couple of minutes after you've had your first climax you will toy with yourself (or get your partner to toy with you) and explore any pleasant and erotic sensations which arise. More detailed suggestions are given in Chapter Nine. Good luck.

Status orgasmicus

This is a rare phenomenon, in which a woman has climax after climax in very rapid succession, with practically no gap in between. It may sound like the fanciful invention of a pornographic novel, but it does occur – and Drs Masters and Johnson did actually observe it in a number of women in their laboratory. They even recorded the women's reactions on scientific instruments.

Basically, what happens is that the lady reaches a climax, and then has another one about two or three seconds later. During the course of about a minute, she may toss off (if you'll forgive the phrase) some twenty or so in fast succession, shrieking loudly on each occasion.

If you do this sort of thing, you are very, very unusual. We hope that the walls of your home are thick.

DO WOMEN EJACULATE DURING ORGASM?

Do women shoot out liquid when they come? Erotic novels almost invariably imply that they should ('As the princess screamed in sheer delight, a torrent of sweet-smelling juice burst forth from her nether regions and flooded over the handsome young Duke's muscular thighs . . .').

In reality, this sort of thing does not happen often. In St Louis, Masters and Johnson watched literally thousands of female climaxes in their lab, but only saw fluid discharged quite rarely – though they did note that a few women apparently leaked urine when they came, or just after.

However, we have received hundreds upon hundreds of letters from fairly distraught readers who quite clearly *do* produce a heck of a lot of some fluid when they climax. In many cases they have said things like: 'I can *never* have a sexual relationship with a man, or get married, because of this terribly embarrassing problem. How could any male cope with a woman who drenches the bed when she orgasms?'

Fortunately, the answer is 'very easily'. It appears that

most men don't mind, and think that if a woman soaks the sheets when she comes, this must be a considerable tribute to the male's virility. So what is this fluid? Well, it's *probably* not urine. Some laboratory research has been done on it since the 1980s – mostly in America – and there does seem to be some evidence that it is a milky liquid, which is said not to stain the sheets (unlike urine) and which *may* come from some structure inside the woman: a structure which could be similar to a man's prostate gland.

Some experts have claimed that this mysterious structure is the same thing as the Famous Female G-spot (see below).

One thing is clear. For the women in question, it's *normal* to produce a jet of this interesting fluid at the moment when they come. Nothing can be done about this, so the best thing to do is to regard it as a sort of 'special sexual bonus'– which your man should be grateful for!

Obviously, it's a good idea for the couple to consider putting a towel under themselves when they make love.

THE FEMALE G-SPOT AND ORGASM

In the medical journals which deal with sexual behaviour, argument continues to rage as to whether there really is such a thing as the much publicised G-spot. All we can tell you is that many women do indeed have a region in the front wall of the vagina which is exceptionally sensitive to sexual stimulation. Rubbing it can, and often does, help a woman reach orgasm.

So it's worth knowing about, and finding out where it is. It's difficult for a woman to feel for herself, so here are our simple instructions for finding it if you're a man:

• ask your partner to lie on her back, with thighs apart;

- making sure that your palm is *facing upwards*, gently slip your well-lubricated index finger into her vagina;
- now make a beckoning gesture with it;
- bending your index finger in this 'come hither' way will bring the pad of your fingertip against the G-spot area;
- if you're in the right region, your partner should experience an unusual but pleasant sensation – which may involve a slight desire to pass water.

Once you've established where the correct spot is, all you have to do is rub it gently. When this caress is combined with clitoris stimulation, your lady should have quite an intense and interesting orgasm.

ORGASM AND CONCEPTION

Female orgasm does not play a very important part in helping conception to occur. In other words, many, many women conceive despite the fact that they didn't climax during that act of intercourse!

But various scientists have claimed that the question of whether a female climaxes can sometimes affect conception. In particular:

- Masters and Johnson say that if a woman has borne children, she stands a better chance of conception by getting sexually excited – but not *quite* coming. This claim is based on a complicated theory involving the fact that the opening of the vagina will remain swollen longer (and hence will tend to hold sperm inside) if the woman does not actually orgasm.
- Dr Desmond Morris, the world-famous zoologist, recently claimed in his international TV series *The Human Animal* – the one which featured a television camera inside a part-time astrologer's vagina while she and her partner

climaxed – that male and female orgasm must be *close together* to give the highest chance of fertilisation.

This claim appears to be based on the filmed evidence – shown in the television series – that during a woman's orgasm, the lower end of her womb (the cervix) thrusts down repeatedly into the pool of the man's semen in her vagina.

We've been in correspondence with Desmond Morris about this, and he believes that the 'downward thrusting' of the womb enables it to suck up the man's sperms. He quotes the research work of Baker and Bellis at Manchester University – which seems to show that if a woman does not climax (or climaxes too early), she will retain less sperms.

ORGASM AND PREGNANCY

Once upon a time, sex used to be 'off limits' during pregnancy but these days it's common for expectant mothers to lead active sex lives all the way through – and to have lots of orgasms.

Is there any danger in this? Well, as we have seen, the womb does *contract* fairly powerfully during a climax, so there might be at least a theoretical risk of causing a miscarriage or early labour. Despite this, most doctors do not advise their patients against sex nowadays. But you should of course be guided by your own obstetrician or family doctor, particularly if you have a tendency to miscarry. We would also urge considerable caution about having any orgasms during the last month of pregnancy, just in case they bring on labour prematurely.

Having said all that, the fact is that large numbers of women do enjoy their climaxes while they're pregnant – particularly in the *middle* months of the pregnancy, when most expectant mums have got over morning sickness and are feeling pretty well.

Indeed, research in America has shown that in those 'middle months', many women experience heightened interest in sex, and have unusually intense orgasms. However, during the last three months of pregnancy some expectant mothers have the bad luck to get cramping pains when they climax. Tell your doctor if this happens.

Orgasms after delivery

Childbirth knocks a heck of a lot out of a woman, and the hormone changes which occur at this time are pretty dramatic. So it's scarcely surprising that quite a lot of women don't want to know about having orgasms for some time afterwards (please see Chapter Four).

However, other women do regain their 'appetite' for sex and for orgasm very quickly after childbirth. A little-known finding of Drs Masters and Johnson is that *breastfeeding mothers are particularly likely to want intercourse and orgasms.*

The reason for this is not clear, but it must be connected with the relationship between suckling and female hormone levels (which are very different in women who do not breastfeed). When a woman who is 'nursing' has an orgasm, the climax may well he accompanied by a sudden squirting of powerful jets of milk from her nipples. This is perfectly normal, and nothing to be alarmed about.

Finally, it's a fact of life that quite a few mothers suddenly find themselves having an unexpected orgasm while they are actually feeding a baby. Some of them feel very guilty about this but there is really no need for guilt at all; it's just due to the fact that the breasts and nipples are very sensitive indeed at this time.

ORGASM AND THE MATURE WOMAN

This section is *good* news! Our survey confirms the findings of various other studies of recent years: women get sexier as they get older. In particular:

- the proportion of women who can reach orgasm increases steadily until well past the age of forty;
- women over forty say that it has become 'easier' to climax than it was;
- multiple orgasm is commonest in the over forties – one forty-plus respondent told us she was having thirty a week;
- in the forties and fifties women are more likely to be able to climax as a result of sexual intercourse *alone* (i.e., with no added stimulation) – an ability that is rare in the young;
- older women seem to worry less about how long it takes them to come;
- the 'nearly there syndrome' (getting to the brink of orgasm but being unable to quite reach it) seems to be less common in the over forties according to our figures.

In fairness, we should add that the *average* number of orgasms among mature women is less than the average number in the twenties. But this seems to be related to the fact that many women in their forties, fifties or sixties do not have partners, or at least not active ones.

However, among mature ladies who do have partners and who are sexually active, it is clear that climaxes very often trip off the clitoris with reassuring speed. (Please see also Chapter Four, which is about how orgasms change during life.)

HOW OFTEN DO WOMEN HAVE ORGASMS?

We do not think that women lie about the frequency of their orgasm in the same way that men do! But we find that they are sometimes a bit vague about the total – which is not surprising, really. It's hard to keep count of whether you've just reeled off five or six, especially when you're having a good time . . .

So we do not set all that great store by answers to questions like 'How many orgasms do you have per week?' Full details can be found in the survey results at the start of this book; see page 12.

THE NEW 'FEMALE ORGASM NOSE SPRAY'

Not long before this book was published, astonishing reports about a new 'female orgasm spray' started appearing. They began with an article in a leading medical journal, written by two Australian doctors. They recounted how they had given a well-known hormone nasal spray to a 26-year-old Melbourne woman, in order to try and help her with breastfeeding.

The effect of the hormone spray was startling: two hours after using it, she noticed that vaginal 'sex fluid' was trickling down her legs, following which she experienced intense sexual desire.

As a result she persuaded her partner to have intercourse. During her orgasms, she noted that her 'uterine [womb] and vaginal contractions were intensified'. She also noticed 'heightened subjective pleasure'.

Next time she used the nose spray, there were similar agreeable effects, lasting for three hours. But when she tried it a couple of weeks later – under slightly different hormonal conditions – there was no response. Following on this report, rumours surfaced in the international press to the effect that nurses in the Obstetric Department of a large British hospital have also discovered the erotic potential of the alleged 'orgasm spray', and are using it before going out on dates.

Will this all turn out to be a red herring?

We do not know. And we would caution anyone who gets hold of this stuff that it may have side-effects. Nevertheless, in the long run science is almost bound to produce a drug which will aid the vast numbers of women who want help to achieve orgasms.

And it could be that this new, wacky-sounding nose spray is the first step along that path . . .

2

THE FEMALE ORGASM – WHY CAN'T IT BE EASIER?

Why Isn't Orgasm Easier For Women? • Female Animals and Orgasm • Orgasm and Conception • How Women Feel about Their Bodies • Women's Feelings about Their Genitals • Feelings about the Clitoris • Feelings about the Vagina • Feelings Which Stem from Visits To the Doctor • Feelings Which Stem from Periods • Learning about Orgasms • Understanding the Differences In Attitudes to Orgasm Between the Sexes

WHY ISN'T ORGASM EASIER FOR WOMEN?

Whether you're a man or a woman, the first thing to realise about female orgasm is this: *it is usually more difficult for women to achieve than male orgasm is for men*.

This is particularly true for younger women. In our survey we asked women of all ages if they could climax whenever they wanted to, **68 per cent said 'No'.**

This is an extraordinary finding! When you consider that most men can come at the drop of a hat (and often expect women to do the same) it is quite staggering that almost seven out of ten females say that they cannot orgasm when they want to.

We then asked if they worried that they took too long to come, **54 per cent said 'Yes'.**

So here we have a situation where more than half of all females are lying in bed with their lovers worrying themselves sick because they think they're taking too long to get there!

On the more positive side, we found that the older women in our sample had learned to climax much more readily, and that they often had multiple orgasms. Some even told us that they could come simply by having their breasts fondled – this is almost unheard of in women under thirty.

The forty-plusses, too, were the group most likely to be able to climax *through intercourse alone* – that is, without any clitoral stimulation. But in our survey only 13 per cent of women said that they usually climaxed through intercourse itself. So much for the common male idea that females should be able to come as a result of being 'poked'!

The majority of the women who filled in our survey – 70 per cent in fact – said that most of their orgasms happened as a result of intercourse *plus* attention to the clitoris. And a further 12 per cent said that they usually climaxed through masturbation, and not through intercourse. (Admittedly, some of them were without a partner at the time.)

It may be that *you* have never climaxed at all, and it's vital for you to realise that you're not alone. Many of the young women we spoke to in connection with this book hadn't had orgasms. And one forty-year-old woman wrote in saying that *she* was still waiting for her first Big O. She added that she lived in hope!

The highly renowned sex therapists Joseph LoPiccolo and Julia Heiman say that 15 to 20 per cent of the women they treat in America have never climaxed. And an even greater percentage of cases involve women who *can* orgasm, but have enormous difficulty in doing so. There are also large numbers of women who can't come with their partners, but only on their own. So, the female orgasm is far from predictable and for many women it's a big problem.

It's just not fair, is it? It would have been so much more agreeable if the female orgasm could have been a simple, enjoyable, reliable part of life – literally a push-button operation! After all, that's *almost* how it is for men.

So what are the explanations for women's difficulty in having orgasms? There seem to be three important ones:

- generally, female animals, including women, are built so that stimulation of the clitoris is quite difficult, especially during intercourse;
- female orgasms aren't necessary for conception, so the human race can reproduce without them;
- human females mostly have all sorts of bad feelings about their bodies – and their sex organs in particular.

FEMALE ANIMALS AND ORGASMS

Very few females in the animal·kingdom are believed to be able to orgasm. It's true that rabbits and other mammals have clitorises, but these are not stimulated when the male leaps on the female from behind. Desmond Morris says that the mating act of the typical baboon lasts only *eight* seconds – which doesn't leave much time for female orgasm. (And we've all known some men like that . . .) But Morris says that only the *human* female has evolved 'an intense orgasmic climax to copulation'. He adds that the females of some other species have been observed to have what he calls 'a mini-orgasm', but nothing that approaches the power and drama of the climactic human female.

So, since most of the female animal kingdom doesn't have orgasms, why do women have the ability to orgasm at all? We asked this question of women up and down the country. Some muttered, defensively, 'Well, why not?' or 'Why the hell shouldn't we?' But no one offered us a stunning or positive answer.

However, men think *they* know. As one chap put it to us: 'Well, it's so much nicer for the man if the woman is enjoying herself!' The female orgasm is a subtle, infuriating, elusive, unpredictable and totally wonderful thing. But is it worth having? And if you can't do it, should you work at it?

You bet!

ORGASM AND CONCEPTION

The second major reason why women don't usually find climaxing as easy as men do is this. *Female orgasm isn't necessary for conceiving a baby.* During the research for this book, one of us (C.W.) spent an afternoon with a group of schoolgirl mums aged between thirteen and fifteen. They'd all produced beautiful babies and had recovered well from the experience of pregnancy and labour.

But while they were perfect biological specimens for motherhood, it turned out that their own sexual pleasure had never entered their minds. I asked them about the acts of intercourse that had made them pregnant and they pulled faces and described them as 'painful' or 'messy' or 'nothing to get worked up about'. And when I asked one young woman (who was busy dandling her baby daughter on her knee) to tell me about her orgasms, she said, 'What's an orgasm?'

In fact *none* of this group of newly delivered girls had ever had a climax in their lives.

HOW WOMEN FEEL ABOUT THEIR BODIES

Now we come to the third reason why orgasms don't seem to happen naturally to women – much as they'd like them to. And this is all to do with how women feel about their bodies.

Compliment any woman on her appearance and she's likely to counter your praise with criticism. 'You're looking great,' we said to a friend the other day. 'I'm half a stone overweight,' she replied. She isn't alone in this misconception. A recent survey in the British magazine *Woman* found that a staggering 84 per cent of women believed themselves to be too fat.

Masses of women hate their pear-shaped form or their small breasts, or their bottoms. In our survey we found that no less than 52 per cent of women actively disliked their own bodies. Furthermore, 24 per cent of women were unhappy about undressing in front of their partners. No wonder many of them had trouble relaxing into a man's arms and having an orgasm.

'Since I've had three children,' said one thirty-year-old, 'I *hate* my tummy.' *Not* surprisingly, her sex life was not in great shape either.

Another woman loathed her stretchmarks and blamed them on two heavy babies, while another claimed that her boobs were the bane of her life since having kids. Once again, in bed they spent more time worrying about their appearance than enjoying orgasms.

But plenty of women who'd never had babies were also miserable about how they looked. An unmarried forty-year-old said that she detested her 'fat stomach, fat waist and drooping boobs'. One woman said that she was too heavy all over – but she did add that her husband liked her that way!

And one fifty year old actually wrote that there was *nothing* about her body that she liked. All in all, tums and bums were top of the hate list, but we also discovered that many females have really negative feelings about their genitals . . .

WOMEN'S FEELINGS ABOUT THEIR GENITALS

Do you know any woman who adores her own genitals? No? Neither do we. Yet most men have a love affair with theirs from the first to the last years of their lives.

Most of us have seen small boys happily fondling their little penises. And any agony aunt will confirm that men well into their seventies and eighties are continuing to conduct a romance with their 'manhoods'.

As for young men, a bride of a few weeks recently wrote to us complaining that her husband spent ages in the bath soaping and admiring his John Thomas. She was pretty keen on it, too, but she couldn't understand his utter preoccupation with it. She wanted to know if he was normal.

He was, of course. And any young bride would be well advised to join her hubby's fan club for his favourite bit. It'll make him *ever* so grateful.

It's sad that women don't have the same love affair with their intimate places. Some, it's true, are desperately attached to their breasts and talk about them in poetic terms, *but* the intensity of their affection doesn't begin to compare with the fanatical devotion that the average man has for his penis.

Worse than that, women frequently describe their genitals as 'ugly' or 'ragged' or 'uneven'. One woman told us that her lover had shaved off her pubic hair for a 'laugh' one night and she had been quite appalled by what had been underneath. 'It looked as though someone had been at me with a pair of those dress-making scissors – pinking shears, I think they call them. It was all kind of serrated. I wanted to cover myself up and couldn't believe that he found me attractive.'

Because of how women feel about the appearance of their genitals, they often find it difficult to relax and enjoy the sensation of receiving oral sex. They just can't believe that men like looking at them so closely. But normal, healthy and sexually well-adjusted men *adore* women's genitals and find them a real turn-on. If women could take that fact on board, their sex lives would definitely improve.

However, even if a woman can be persuaded that she looks attractive 'down below' she often has terrible hang-ups about her smell and taste. Here's an example. As agony aunt of the TV satellite channel UK Living's 'Agony Hour' one of us (C.W.) answers queries on vast numbers of viewers' sex problems. One guy rang to say that he was completely baffled by the fact that his wife was refusing oral sex. They had previously always enjoyed this method of making love and his missus had experienced some of her most intense orgasms that way. But in recent weeks she had gone right off it, though she was still happy to fellate her hubby.

We chatted about this and what emerged was that though she loved having her husband lick away at her clitoris, she hated him kissing her on the lips afterwards. It was the taste, you see. She thought it was ghastly and it ruined the act of love for her when she caught the flavour of her own genitals from her husband's mouth. So he agreed not to kiss her lips after cunnilingus. And last time I heard, oral sex was back on the menu!

This is an extreme case, but many females will understand just what that wife felt. Yet the average male finds the taste and smell of his beloved's genitals absolutely delightful. Ladies, please take note.

Women's unease with their pink bits may well stem from the fact that they're all hidden away. A little girl tends to think she has *nothing* between her legs, while her brother is blessed with a rather interesting dangly thing that he's clearly delighted with. Unlike her, he usually has a name for it, too – something like Cocky, Willy, Micky, Pizzle, The Man, Dong or Ralph (!).

It's true that in some posh homes a small girl is taught to call the whole area her 'vulva'. And a large number of women brought up in the 1940s and 1950s refer to it all as their 'front bottom' – but this makes no sense at all.

The fact is that no one explains the complexity of her genitals to the average small girl. Was any woman ever brought up in the knowledge that she had a small hole for peeing from, a hole which one day babies would come out of, and a little bud that was pleasurable to touch? If you were, then count yourself lucky, as you're in a very small minority.

It's not uncommon, even nowadays, for some adult women to believe that they pee from the same hole as they bleed from during a period. In fact everything about the way women are made seems contrived to keep things secret and somehow rather shameful.

'The whole damn caboodle is flawed,' complained one forty-year-old in our survey. 'Women's genitals are a massive design fault!'

FEELINGS ABOUT THE CLITORIS

Many women that we spoke to told us that they were well into their adult lives before they knew that they had a clitoris.

Some took even longer to find out what it was for! This must stem from the fact that girls aren't told that they have one. In fact we couldn't find anyone who'd been given a name for it as a child. Worse than that, most women *still* don't have a name for it as adults! And, 'Could you put your hand on my . . . errr . . .' doesn't convey very much to the average lover!

The French call the clitoris *'le cli-cli'* which sounds rather sweet. But most women, if they name it at all, either say it in full, which is very formal, or resort to the language of soft porn magazines and call it a clit – which isn't a nice word at all. It also rhymes with slit – which is equally nasty and something many men call the vagina.

FEELINGS ABOUT THE VAGINA

Unlike the clitoris, vaginas *are* sometimes given names by adult women. And these names can be affectionate – like fanny (in Britain only – not in the USA, where 'fanny' means 'ass'), crumpet or pussy. In an act of bravado a woman *may* refer to her vagina as her cunt. But 'cunt' is also such an abusive, swearing word, much used by men, that most women don't feel comfortable with it.

As we've already seen, women can feel very uneasy about their natural scent and taste. They write in, in enormous numbers, to magazine health pages about vaginal smell and even more commonly about discharge. In fact some women worry obsessively about the state and odour of their vaginas when they are, in fact, entirely normal. Then there's size. Young women are frequently convinced that their vaginas are too small. Often their early sexual experiences make them think this. But usually all that's wrong is that they've been having sex with unskilled lovers who fail to get them well enough lubricated before penetration.

And childbirth brings its own vaginal problems. Women

worry that they're too large after a baby or two, and many of them are very unhappy about the less-than-beautiful stitching they've received after their delivery.

So, all in all, the vagina is often perceived as an area of trouble for a woman – when it should be perceived as a nice, warm recess that not only provides endless joy for her mate, but warm, contracting and delicious feelings for her too.

FEELINGS WHICH STEM FROM VISITS TO THE DOCTOR

Unlike men, women frequently have to expose their sex organs to doctors. They have smears and internal examinations; they're fitted for caps and coils and, of course, they're pulled all over the place once they're pregnant.

Opening your legs to a doctor is an odd experience, even if he or she is gentle and kind. The doctor may touch where a lover would, but a woman must switch off her normal responses in that area because they're not appropriate in this situation. But later that day her own partner may approach her in much the same way as the doctor did earlier. Then she's supposed to be switched on and instantly orgasmic. Is it any wonder she's confused?

A woman has to compartmentalise in this way from a very early age, so it's perhaps not surprising that her mind and her body don't always link up quickly to tell her when this 'touching' of her is OK and desirable and nice, as opposed to clinical, and something simply to be endured.

FEELINGS WHICH STEM FROM PERIODS

Periods are part of this compartmentalisation. For many women periods are painful and embarrassing – even very young girls can have terrible monthly cramps. A teenager we know has severe period pain and told us: 'I don't care what the women's movement says, if there *is* a God, he's definitely male!'

It's important to realise that girls can be as young as nine or ten when they start their periods. A few of these haven't even been told about menstruation as their parents or teachers assumed that it wouldn't happen for years. It's bad enough dealing with the discomfort and the mess when you're grown-up, but it can be seriously traumatic for a child. No wonder that such children may grow up with negative rather than positive feelings about their vaginas.

Women and girls are also very bothered about the smell of periods. We've asked men about this and they say that they can't smell anything when their partners have the curse. But females frequently worry about the odour of menstrual blood. And several women we spoke to recalled very unhappy memories of the smell of their early monthlies.

One 48-year-old remembered hers as if it were yesterday:

'My first period had just started and I had to go to school with this very heavy flow. I remember these beastly cumbersome pads that my mother had given me. And I could smell this awful stench. Thank God I was at an all-girls school, or I think I would have died. But as it was I felt very pongy and was very upset about it.

   The most stupid thing is that I never discussed it, either with my mum, or my friends. But I don't think I was unusual in that. In those days you just suffered in silence.'

When we talked about orgasms with this same woman, she confessed that she'd been a very late developer. She believed that her negative feelings about her body and its functions had held her back and that it took years before she was remotely interested in sex.

'I was certainly the last girl in my group to have a boyfriend, and though I learned to masturbate to orgasm when I was twenty, I didn't "go all the way" with my boyfriend till I was twenty-two.'

Several other forty-somethings recalled how they hated their bodies once they'd started menstruating. And some of them told me that when they realised there were such things as tampons, they'd asked their mums if they could change to them. They all reported that their mothers had assured them that virgins couldn't wear them!

One woman said that her mother made her feel a tramp just for asking.

All in all, then, it seems likely that most girls first become acquainted with the vagina when blood is flowing from it and they're feeling achey and unwell. So is it so very strange that a woman has to *learn* to feel excited and enthusiastic about the same part of her in different circumstances?

LEARNING ABOUT ORGASMS

Our survey showed that even though most women had been told something about sex by their mothers, only 6 per cent of them had been told about orgasms. A 51-year-old explained that she felt her whole sex life had been blighted through lack of education and knowledge. She actually had her first orgasm at the age of fourteen but didn't know what it was. And a professional woman in her thirties said: 'My mother thought she was very open about sex and prided herself on giving us all possible information – but I think she'd have died rather than say the word "orgasm" let alone explain what it was.'

So the situation is that 94 per cent of girls grew up without having been told about orgasms by their parents. Our information is that very few hear about them in school classes, either. Is it any wonder then that so many of them wander into adult life without a clue about this important and vastly enjoyable female function?

UNDERSTANDING THE DIFFERENCES IN ATTITUDES TO ORGASM BETWEEN THE SEXES

Finally, it's important to realise that men and women have very different attitudes to orgasm. And since most women have their orgasms with men – or want to – it may help to look briefly at the basic differences between the genders.

Women can be highly sexed and horny, but according to sex therapists Joseph LoPiccolo and Julia Heiman, even for a woman who can have orgasms easily, a climax doesn't occur every time she makes love. The average for easily orgasmic females is 70 per cent to 80 per cent of the time.

It's difficult for men to understand how women's hormonal changes work, and why one day they're panting for sex while on the next they resent being touched. But if *that's* difficult, it's equally hard for women to understand the urgent, perpetual sex drive of most men.

Did you know that the average bloke will have some 9000 orgasms during his lifetime? That's an awful lot of damp patches! In fact, it's over thirty litres of ejaculate. So males clearly have a driving urge to pump this stuff out!

Many men appear to have a mental ideal of how many orgasms per week they need. Not only that, they often believe that if they don't *get* that many, their health will suffer. When men are refused sex in a relationship they often become very petty – occasionally violent. A kind of panic sets in as they contemplate the prospect of no sex for the night . . . the week . . . the year . . .

In this panic, a young man whose partner has temporarily denied him sex may keep demanding it and become more than usually sexually voracious. Frequently this happens when the wife is a new mum and exhausted by childbirth, possibly breastfeeding, and looking after the baby. The young husband has already had his nose put out of joint by the child and now suffers the ultimate rejection of no sex.

Counsellors for Relate – the British Marriage Guidance organisation – advise a woman in this situation to tell her man when she thinks she *will* want sex again. Once he knows that the ban isn't permanent, the average lad stops behaving like a crazed animal and may accept the amended schedule, even if he doesn't agree with it.

You can see just how sexually driven men are by looking at the gay community. Though many gays have long, and deeply committed relationships, others don't. For instance a representative of Outrage, the UK gay pressure group, was recently reported as saying that he'd had 300 partners in his life to date. And before AIDS changed sexual behaviour, gay men would report up to fifty different encounters – obviously not all to orgasm – in gay clubs in one evening.

Women can't compete with that! And most of them wouldn't want to.

If there's a comparably urgent need in women it's for love and appreciation and closeness and touching. Of course many men like those things, too, but for them the goal of orgasm is of paramount importance. Women *do* want orgasms. Some who responded to our survey even said that orgasms were essential for good health. But females rarely have the appetite of the male.

Some men have told us that their last thought before actually ejaculating has been: 'I wonder how soon I can do this again?'

That's how they are, bless them. And though plenty of them will feel anxious sometimes about keeping their erections, most of them will go through their entire lives without worrying about the ability to come. How totally unlike a woman!

Many, many women have helped us with this book. Their experiences – the true stories of real people – will help you realise that others have the same difficulties as you, or feel awkward about the same sort of things. Knowing this should give you confidence in your quest either to *become* orgasmic or just to have better or more reliable orgasms.

You might even laugh a bit – and that'll help more than anything.

3

THE FIRST ORGASM IN WOMEN

At What Age Does it Happen? • How Do Women Achieve Their First Orgasm? • Feelings About It • Orgasm at First Intercourse • Vibrators • First Orgasm Later in Life.

AT WHAT AGE DOES IT HAPPEN?

The truly amazing fact about first orgasm is that it can happen at virtually any age. As we told you in Chapter Two, we know of women in their forties and older still waiting to experience the Big O. But the women we surveyed experienced their first orgasms between the tender age of five and the late forties.

Women are good at remembering 'firsts' in their life, like the first day at school, the name of the first boy they ever kissed, and the first time they had intercourse. And, it seems that the magical moment of first orgasm is something else that they recall *very* clearly.

But while girls can't wait to tell their best mates about snogging a new lad, or losing their virginity, very, very few ever discuss that monumental leap in their sex lives when they climax for the first time. Over and over again, women told us that *we* were the only people with whom they'd ever discussed their first orgasms.

But the youngest, the woman who was only five when she experienced her first, was no freak. There was a six-year-old in our survey and several others who were ten or under. However, we found that the largest number of ladies were eighteen when they first rang the bell. And the next biggest group were nineteen.

A fifth of our sample, though, were twenty-something before they got there. A smaller number were in their thirties before they finally struck gold, and a few were in their forties – which shows you should never give up!

One of those was forty-one when she finally 'came' and her story, which we'll tell at the end of this chapter, is a very emotional and inspiring one.

HOW DO WOMEN ACHIEVE THEIR FIRST ORGASM?

Considering the tender age of some orgasmic females, it should perhaps come as no surprise that our survey shows that the commonest way in which today's women first reached orgasm was masturbation. In our survey a massive 47 per cent of females said they had their initial climax through 'touching themselves up'. Next came intercourse. 32 per cent of women in our survey had reached the Big O for the first time during an act of intercourse – which is possibly a little surprising when you consider how difficult it is to reach a climax through intercourse alone.

Petting, or love play, was third with 20 per cent of our female correspondents getting there in that way. This included a minority who'd had first orgasms through oral sex. And finally a small number said that they'd first climaxed while asleep and having a sexy dream.

You may be shocked by the fact that so many women say that they first came through masturbating, but there is much less guilt attached to masturbation these days (and a good thing too), so it may well be that more young females are going in for DIY sex.

FEELINGS ABOUT IT

We asked women to tell us how they felt about achieving that first climax, whether it was through masturbation, intercourse, petting or whatever.

Masturbation

Those few women in our survey who climaxed well before puberty all said that they had had an interest in their sex organs from an early age.

Several of these women said that they thought the warm feelings they experienced were unique to them. And once they'd worked out how they got them, whether it was by rolling around on a pillow, or by rubbing their favourite teddy between their legs, they did it frequently.

One woman said that having discovered this marvellous game, her parents no longer had any problem getting her to bed at night, because once there she would rock herself to sleep with her furry rabbit between her legs and would almost always have an orgasm. Of course she didn't know what it was then.

It's sad that, for some reason, many women who had experienced orgasm as children told us that climaxing did not come easily as an adult with a partner. One 22-year-old woman said: 'I had no idea that what I was striving for was the feeling I'd had so easily with my teddy'.

From our researches it seems that many women simply grew out of their early masturbatory play. Others said that they were punished for it and grew up feeling guilty whenever they felt a special warmth or a twinge of excitement in their genitals.

Whatever the exact experience of those women who remembered climaxing as children, it's clear that childhood orgasm is not the heart-stopping number that it is for someone in her late teens, or for a mature woman. A 48-year-old who filled in our survey told us in graphic detail about the night she masturbated to her first orgasm at the age of nineteen.

Apparently, sex was rarely mentioned at home, but she had discovered that her father had a collection of racy novels hidden away. These were full of unlikely sex scenes where titled ladies would take lowly servants for lovers and were quickly overcome by effortless, earth-shattering ecstasy. Our correspondent said:

'I wasn't sure what to make of all this. I had never let a

boy do anything but give me the dryest of kisses as I'd
been brought up to "save myself for marriage".

'I had heard that sex was supposed to be nice for
women, but these books suggested to me that there
was more to it than that. Anyway, I took to reading these
novels when my dad was out. I was terrified of being
found out so I treated them with great care and always
put them back in their secret hiding place exactly as I'd
found them. My interest in the stories grew and grew
and I realised that, as I read them, I was breathing
faster and feeling a warm thrilling feeling down below.

'One day, when I was nineteen I put my hand inside
my knickers and started rubbing my clitoris. As a child
I'd fondled myself around the whole area of my genitals
and found it comforting, but this was different. The
urge to touch and rub was compulsive. I didn't know
what it was all leading to, but whatever it was, I wanted
it, desperately.

'One particular afternoon I was becoming so excited
that I got frightened and decided to stop. So I put the
book away and played some records to calm myself
down. But that night in bed, my fingers had a mind of
their own and kept returning to my clitoris. It felt really
great. Soon I was breathing heavily and, much to my
amazement, I found myself kind of moving rhythmically
on my back up and down the bed. It was so strange that
I tried to stop, but I couldn't. (The funny thing is that I
don't move around like this when I masturbate now.)

'Soon I was locked into this movement and my
fingers must have been working overtime . It was
absolutely marvellous and I knew suddenly that I wasn't
going to stop till 'it' had happened.

'And then it did – this incredible explosion. It was
really intense and wonderful, but frightening, too. I
remember leaping out of bed and looking at myself in
my dressing-table mirror . My pupils were huge and I

was very flushed. I searched into my eyes for a sign that
I'd lost my innocence – that's how I thought of it. I was
delighted to have had this grown-up feeling, but
worried that everyone would be able to see that I'd
done it. I definitely felt that what I had done was almost
as bad as having intercourse with a boy before
marriage.

'I changed a lot within the next few years and had sex
with several men before I married. And I never felt
guilty again – not like I did about my first orgasm. It's
funny how you never tell anyone about it. I had really
close girlfriends but I never mentioned it. But it was
certainly one of the most significant things that ever
happened to me and I can remember the huge
excitement of it now. In fact I feel really turned on just
writing about it.

'The funny thing was that having found this magical
experience I couldn't leave myself alone. For the next
few weeks I was pressing myself up against the corners
of tables when no one was looking and squeezing my
legs together while travelling on trains or buses.

'I just couldn't get enough and used to climax about
four times every day. It made me feel marvellous. I'd
been a very tense teenager and had suffered from
persistent headaches and aches in my neck and
shoulder. Suddenly they'd all gone. And I remember
thinking to myself that if everyone did what I was doing,
no one would have silly little illnesses or be miserable,
I just thought I'd discovered a miracle!'

Intercourse

Of the women who told us that their first experience of
orgasm came through intercourse, the youngest was only
seventeen. Almost half of the women were into their twenties
or even thirties. Most of them were in loving relationships

and the vast majority of them had a lot of clitoral stimulation during the act of intercourse that gave them their first climax.

A 23-year-old university student in Scotland described what happened to her the very first time:

'I was introduced to sex from the reproductive point of view by my mum. I also had some sex education at school, but I never even *heard* the word "orgasm" till I was seventeen or eighteen.

'My first boyfriend was very selfish and not at all interested in my pleasure. I began to realise that things were wrong so I talked to my sister. She told me about my clitoris and gave me moral support and some general hints. The breakthrough came when a male friend said that I needed someone who would show me what sex was really all about. I was intrigued because up to that time I'd had no real interest at all.

'Sex with him was a revelation – here was a man who was more interested in my pleasure than his. And a man who wanted me to have my pleasure *first* !

'He helped me so much and eventually I had an orgasm with him. I now see orgasm as a mental thing. You have to love yourself in order to let it happen. I still have to tell myself it's OK to have pleasure and to indulge in sex, as I absorbed a lot of negative thinking from my mother during childhood and also from the Catholic religion.

'I still don't orgasm easily and think it will be years before I rid myself of all my hang-ups. But I shall always be grateful that I was brought to my first orgasm with such care and love. Because ever since then I've known that no matter how difficult it seems, I *can* climax, because I've done it before.'

Petting

Some first climaxes through petting took place very early. By petting we mean playing around with breasts and genitals. The youngest in our sample was eleven, though this is not an age at which we would recommend it. Most of those who were petted to their first orgasms were in their mid to late teens when it happened. But for quite a few it didn't happen till their early twenties.

We noticed that the 'petting' group of women seemed to have got involved with men earlier than the women whose first orgasms occurred through masturbation or intercourse. Though they experienced their first climaxes through petting, two-thirds of them went on to have sexual intercourse before their eighteenth birthdays.

As a group, it appears that today they are highly-sexed and pleased with their sex lives, even though many of them are now in their fifties. A substantial minority of the 'petting' group reached the first orgasm of their lives through oral sex, which is maybe not too surprising when you consider the intense stimulus it gives to females.

A happily married woman from Scunthorpe wrote to tell us of her first climax:

'I was twenty and it happened with a boyfriend I loved very much. Before then sex was something I could take or leave. I did it just to please the man I was with.

'I read lots of books with my girlfriends and I know we all wondered what orgasms were. We definitely wanted them, but didn't know how to get them. Then one night, my boyfriend gave me oral sex and for some reason I let him go on for longer than I really felt I should have done. And that was it. Wow!

'The secret, I discovered, was to lie back and let your lover entertain you, and to stop being in a rush to get on to intercourse. That kind of information wasn't available in the books we were reading, so you had to find it out for yourself.

'I still love oral sex and I'm very, very lucky as my husband absolutely adores giving it to me. I believe it's vital to know that the man is enjoying it as much as you.'

During sleep

Unlike men who are quite likely to have their first orgasm during a 'wet dream', we've found that few women seem to have orgasms in their sleep. And only 2 per cent of the women we surveyed had their very first orgasms that way.

A woman, now in her forties, told us how it happened to her:

'I was about sixteen. I didn't have a boyfriend but I was wildly in love with my dentist, who of course was happily married with children. It's amazing, when I look back, how strong my love and lust for him were, even though they were totally unrequited. Thank God I never made a fool of myself by telling the poor man.

'Anyway I used to go to sleep thinking of 'Mr C.' and he was my first waking thought, too. Then one night I had a wonderful dream. In it the handsome, softly spoken, dreamy dentist was making love to me. I was quite an innocent sixteen-year-old and had only the sketchiest idea of how this was achieved in real life. But in my dream, I was supremely confident and I can remember to this day how as he entered me, I raised my hips up to meet him and was suddenly filled with this golden excitement.

'I woke immediately, breathless and filled with this glorious, thrilling feeling. I remember it took me ages to calm down afterwards.

'As far as I know, I wasn't fondling myself in my sleep. I certainly didn't wake up with my hands on my genitals and I had never masturbated at that time. I didn't know for years afterwards that what I'd experienced was called an "orgasm". I just thought I'd learned through my dream that sex brought with it this amazing thrill.

'Of course I imagined that when I finally had sexual intercourse it would be just like that – absolutely lovely with no effort. It wasn't – unfortunately.'

ORGASM AT FIRST INTERCOURSE

A sizeable minority of women had an orgasm the first time they had intercourse: 18 per cent of women in our survey told us that they'd rung the bell on that very first occasion. Most of these women had already had their first orgasms through masturbation or petting, but we know of a number of women who actually came for the very first time during their initiation into full sex.

One elderly woman told us, rather shyly, that she had had her first orgasm with her husband on her wedding night, which was the first time they'd made love:

'I'd been brought up very strictly and we hadn't been allowed to spend much time together before we were married.

'We were certainly deeply attracted to each other, but never did anything beyond kissing – except before we got wed he sometimes managed to feel my breasts.

'I realise I'm very lucky when I hear how other women have such trouble reaching orgasm. It just seemed such a natural thing that night. I can't say it was *always* that easy, but we learned things together. And we were always able to talk – that was the main thing. Also we liked each other a lot – still do.'

Another 'first orgasm-first intercourse' experience that we

know about, was rather different:

> 'It was with an older, divorced man,' said a London woman of 38. I was in love with him, or maybe with the idea of being in love with him. He was very sophisticated and I knew he'd had loads of lovers. It was in the late seventies and having many partners was very cool at the time.
>
> 'Anyway, he took me to bed and spent what seemed like hours and hours petting me and giving me oral sex. I was really fired up. He didn't know I was a virgin as I was ashamed of that – most of my friends had already had sex by then.
>
> 'Anyway, when he did enter me, I felt something kind of yield inside me. Perhaps he realised then that he was the first. Happily there was no pain – I expect this was because I was practically on fire by then. He was very good at it and somehow kept rubbing my clitoris all the time. I think we finished up with him behind me, fondling me as he rode in and out of me. It was fantastic.
>
> 'He had a lot of self control and only came after I had. I just freaked out. I felt I almost fainted – I certainly saw stars. The awful thing is that he finished with me soon afterwards. He wasn't looking for a relationship, just sex. But I shall always be grateful to him.
>
> 'I had several mediocre experiences after that and quickly realised that not all men bother with you or your pleasure. But at least I knew what I was aiming for. Eventually I found that kind of expertise *and* love. That's a winning combination!'

VIBRATORS

Many women who wrote to us, or who took part in our

survey had downright horrid sex lives in their teens and twenties. And plenty of them wanted to tell us that, far from thrilling to their first act of intercourse, or tripping off several orgasms as soon as a man got his hand near their intimate parts, learning how to orgasm was a real sweat.

Some women told us that they were profoundly unhappy for years with their inability to orgasm. Others didn't know that they weren't having an orgasm. Some thought that the stirring in their loins when they began to get excited *was* a climax. It was nice, but nothing special, so they were completely baffled about why everyone else seemed to think that sex was so marvellous.

We'll be devoting much of Chapter Eight to helping women reach a climax for the first time, but since so many women mentioned one particular method of achieving a long-awaited orgasm – namely a vibrator – we thought it was worth mentioning here.

A Manchester woman wrote telling us how a new partner *and* a vibrator opened up a whole different world for her:

'I was married and had three children, I thought our sex life was OK even though the marriage itself became a very unhappy one. Then after I divorced I met an older man – a widower – and we fell in love. Eventually we embarked on a relationship that included sex. I enjoyed this very much.

'But after about six months, my man asked me what he could do to give me an orgasm. And for the first time ever I realised that there should be something else to sex, which I'd never had. So, my lover bought me a vibrator and introduced it into our love making.

'We had some good sessions but, according to my partner, I still hadn't had an orgasm. Next he suggested that I played around with my new sex toy when I was alone. He thought this would give me confidence and that I would find out what pleased me.

'I tried this, one quiet afternoon, and after about half an hour I did have an orgasm – the most fantastic feeling I'd ever had. I felt like the cat who'd had the cream and couldn't stop smiling. When my partner came in from work, he didn't have to ask what had happened. He just smiled as he told me what a beautiful expression I had on my face.

'He took me to bed immediately and I managed to orgasm with the vibrator again. My lover was wildly excited at the sight of this and came very quickly. But after a break for kisses and cuddles we started again. He penetrated me but I kept the vibrator on my clitoris and it was so utterly marvellous that we both came again – this time together.

'Four years later our love life is still extraordinary and I can honestly say that this wonderful man has turned my life around.'

FIRST ORGASM LATER IN LIFE

As we said at the start of this chapter, orgasm can happen at virtually any age. So for anybody reading this book who has not yet got there, please don't despair. Some women who are later than average in achieving the Big O get there because they meet an unselfish man who is determined that they should enjoy sex fully – like our heroine with the vibrator in the last section.

One of our favourite contributions from women who answered our survey came from a 45-year-old who'd had to wait till the age of thirty-four for her first orgasm:

'I'd lost my virginity at eighteen to the man I was shortly to marry. It was OK – nothing awful, but not very nice either. I do remember that I was pleased to have lost my virginity. I thought I must look different and I certainly wanted to.

'We had a routine kind of marriage and children. I suppose I thought my life was as good as I could expect. I didn't know that I'd never had an orgasm, so I couldn't understand why other people seemed to think that sex was so great.

'Part of my trouble was that my mum had been very uptight about sex and never told me anything. Even today she's terribly ignorant about it all.

'I was working as a dancing teacher and I grew friendly with someone who taught in the same building. My marriage was pretty boring and I suppose I was ready for a fling. Anyway I liked this man a lot.

'We went to bed. I really wanted to, even though I still didn't know that I had a clitoris or what orgasms were. But by the end of the afternoon I knew. My lover was sweet and patient and he really worked at stroking and caressing me and finding out what turned me on.

'Soon I was trembling and panting. I remember thinking, "Oh my God, I'm having a stroke – I've really done it now." And then I came. It was mind-blowing.

'Life has never been the same again. I didn't stay with my lover, but I'll always remember him with affection. Not surprisingly, my marriage ended. I don't think there was any way it could have survived. Not once I knew what I'd been missing.

'I'm married for a second time now to a man who loves to give me orgasms and I have between four and eight every week. I may have been a late-starter but I'm making up for lost time now!'

Other women realise quite far into adult life that they are missing something and determine to take matters into their own hands – literally.

We end this chapter with the remarkable story of one

woman's quest for sexual fulfilment. We'll call her Betty.
Betty's earliest memories are of herself as a happy, lively
child with a great love of life. But she told us how this
happiness was squashed out of her by a stern and
uncompromising mother with steely eyes.

Betty can remember that as little more than a baby, she
overheard rows between her parents where her father
hurled abuse at his wife and called her 'frigid'.

As Betty grew older she understood something of what
this meant. And her mother actually told her, as a teenager,
that she was proud of the fact that she'd always refused sex
except on the occasions that she wanted to have children.
Betty wrote:

> 'Whenever smutty jokes were heard or there was
> kissing on the TV, I saw mother's grey, hard eyes. I
> suppose I got used to them.
>
> 'As I reached puberty my mother seemed to become
> obsessed with my sexuality. I was told that touching
> yourself below was a mortal sin for which your soul
> would burn in hell. She also kept stressing that the only
> time a woman should submit to sex was when a baby
> was planned.
>
> 'As you can imagine, I entered into womanhood
> immature and naïve. But I liked the company of men
> and enjoyed dancing and flirting. However, if any man
> tried to kiss me, or mentioned sex, I went cold. This is
> a 'cold' no one should experience – hate and
> repugnance of the touch of another human being and of
> their love.
>
> 'I met my husband when I was twenty. Throughout
> our married life I hated sex. I hated his touch and did
> my best to avoid it. Tempers became frayed, but we
> loved each other and clung on together through our
> troubles.
>
> 'I'd turned forty and had two teenage children.

Suddenly I was horrified that I couldn't speak to them about sex, so I sat back and looked over my life. Then something made me get up and look at myself in the mirror. As I stared at my reflection and saw my tatty clothes, tatty hair, and a total lack of make-up, I gasped in horror. Standing, looking out at me was *my mother.*

'At that moment I realised what had happened to me. I began to forgive my mother, as I realised that she must have once been a child, too, and God knows what she had suffered to make her like that. But I also realised that I was *not* my mother and didn't need to behave like her. And that very night I began to change.

'I lay in a luxurious bath, bubbles practically coming out of my ears, and instead of the usual quick wash avoiding looking at any part of me, little by little I began to explore my body.

'Day after day I did this until I found a place which made shivers run down my spine and goosebumps appear on my flesh. I was frightened and stopped, but the next night I tried again. And then I went that one bit further until one night I couldn't stop. It was like an itch. To scratch makes this itch worse and tremendously powerful. Don't get me wrong, not painful, but . . . yes, painful. Yet to stop would be agony.

'As this itch grows, every marvellous feeling that you can think of takes place. Your breathing is different and your heart misses beats or triples its beating. Then your brain feels as if it must explode and your mouth has this stupid habit of opening and the saliva dripping out.

'Why men find us attractive at this time, I don't know!

'Then all at once, muscles, teeth and nails tense almost like cramp, but opposite to cramp, sending ripples of pure pleasure through every millimetre of your being. At first volcanic, then as each ripple ends, getting smaller and smaller until you collapse, exhausted, but so relaxed you could just have spent thousands of pounds on a massage!

'That's how it was. But after that first time I turned my attention to my poor husband and found to the great joy of both of us that I loved sex.'

4

ORGASMS THROUGH LIFE

They Do Change as You Get Older! • Orgasms in the Teens • Orgasms in the Twenties • Orgasms in the Thirties • Orgasms in the Forties • Orgasms in the Fifties • Orgasms in the Sixties And Beyond • As Women Get More Orgasmic, Men Get *Less* • Solo Orgasm in the Later Years

THEY DO CHANGE AS YOU GET OLDER!

Orgasms change *throughout* your life. For instance, plenty of women have told us that they experienced deeper and more complete orgasms once they met a partner they truly loved. Others complained of mediocre sex during unhappy first marriages, but discovered how to have reliable and intense orgasms when they settled with someone new, who was keen to give them a good time.

But even those who've remained with the same partner through most of their sex lives have told us that their climaxes have altered as they've got older.

Vast numbers of women said that climaxing got easier with age and that with the passing years they developed the knack of having multiple orgasms. Some mid-life women have also told us that they had their best sex *ever* after the menopause. This may come as a bit of a shock to our younger readers but it does give them something to look forward to!

Unfortunately, though most women become more easily orgasmic with age, they may nonetheless fail to have as many orgasms as they would like. Some claim they can't because they don't have as much energy as they used to. Others say that their orgasms are so powerful and all-consuming that they need fewer sex sessions than they had when they were younger. But there's another factor: the male partners of so many of these ripe and sexy women are simply not as sexually driven as they were as young men. As we'll see later in the chapter, with older couples it's often the man who's claiming that he's too tired for a spot of rumpy-pumpy, or pleading to be let off sex because he has a headache!

ORGASMS IN THE TEENS

We can't stress too strongly how much we believe that experimenting with sex with boys is best left till girls are sixteen or over. Girls are *much* likelier to have a happy sexual initiation as they get a bit older, because they're more confident in themselves, and more discriminating in their choice of boy. Also, *very* importantly, our statistics show that the later they start having sex, the more likely they are to use contraception.

We spoke to a number of *young* teenagers – thirteen- and fourteen-year-olds – who had had full sex. All of them said that they didn't enjoy it. And *none* of them had had an orgasm during sex. Indeed the possibility of real pleasure didn't seem to have occurred to them. It's very distressing that even at the end of the twentieth century some very young girls are giving their bodies to boys because they believe that's the only way to keep a boyfriend.

As they frequently discover, coming over with the goods doesn't guarantee that the lad will stick around. And meanwhile the young lass is having sex with absolutely *no* expectation of orgasm or of *any* sexual pleasure herself.

We had some very honest replies to our survey from some *older* female teenagers who were also having fairly miserable sex lives. Many of them were still waiting for their first orgasm.

So though the media tend to portray modern-day female adolescents as being rampant for sex and busy having climaxes we found the reality to be somewhat different.

Also, there are plenty of girls who are too shy (or who have too many hang-ups) to find romance or sexual pleasure. One unhappy eighteen-year-old girl told us that she was a virgin and had had no sex experience whatsoever. She didn't masturbate and had never had an orgasm. She reckoned that her late development was due to 'a very strict upbringing and religious teaching'. Another nineteen-year-old, who'd lost her virginity at sixteen, didn't have a current boyfriend and felt that she had serious hang-ups about masturbation, intercourse, and oral sex.

She also said that her overwhelming embarrassment was the major reason why she couldn't reach orgasm with a partner, whenever she was in a relationship.

As we've said elsewhere in this book, a women's confidence in her appearance plays a big part in her ability to let go and have orgasms. For example, a nineteen-year-old who felt that she was pressurised into full sex at fifteen and hated it, was distressed by what she described as 'my lack of waist and big belly'. As a consequence, undressing in front of a partner has always been sheer torment for her. She doesn't have a boyfriend at present and says that she can't orgasm at all.

We certainly would never want any young woman to abandon her religious belief, or lose her virginity before she is ready to, but if you are a teenager who feels badly troubled by sexual hang-ups, then it's a good idea to seek experienced counselling from a youth advisory clinic.

However, it isn't all gloom and doom in the teens – far from it. But it's noticeable that most of the young women to whom we spoke who were happy with their sex lives had clung to their virginity till the age of sixteen or older, and had refused to be pressurised into having sex before they were ready.

One nineteen-year-old described her love life as 'wonderful' and told us that she regularly had six orgasms a week with her boyfriend, who is loving and gentle and has taken the time to read books about how to make women happy.

Many of the girls told us that they climaxed principally through love play, and *none* of the teenagers we surveyed found any satisfaction in intercourse unless they had clitoral stimulation too. When they *did* have intercourse they liked to choose a position where their clitorises could get plenty of attention from their partner or themselves – doggy-style scored particularly highly with this age group, as did positions where the woman was on top.

Oral sex seems especially popular with late teenage girls and several of them told us that this form of sex produced their most intense orgasms.

ORGASMS IN THE TWENTIES

Women in their twenties find that this is a period of mixed fortunes orgasmically! And yet it's a decade when many of them clock up plenty of climaxes. Let's look at various groups:

Early developers – ten years on

We've seen already how often young girls offer sex to their boyfriends in order to keep them, despite the fact that they're getting no sexual pleasure themselves. When we meet these same girls in their twenties they're frequently burdened with several kids and a boring relationship with a neglectful boyfriend or husband.

As one woman of twenty-two with two children explained:

'We've been together since I was sixteen. I felt very grown up, setting up house before all my friends, but now I can see what I've missed.

'I know through reading women's magazines and from TV programmes that there's something called an orgasm that I don't get. I want to have it, just like other women, but sometimes I think I'll never be able to.'

Well, she *could* if she and her husband got some good sex education – or embarked on the 'step-by-step' plans later in this book.

Another young woman of twenty-five told us how after ten years with the same man and no orgasm, she had had an affair with someone else to try to get one. Unfortunately all hell had broken loose as a result and the worst of it is that she *still* hasn't had a climax.

Many twenty-somethings like her are in a *Catch-22* situation. There'll be no end of trauma if they make the changes that might lead to happiness and sexual fulfilment. And there'll be nothing but misery ahead if they don't. Unfortunately, the ability to orgasm early in life doesn't guarantee foolproof orgasms with a partner in the twenties.

The story of one 24-year-old in our survey certainly bears this out. Though she had her first orgasm at five, she told us that nowadays she fakes orgasm from time to time and has, on occasions, been left quite frustrated by her partner. She says:

'He wants a lot of position-changing and this makes me lose my build-up to orgasm. I can climax in the missionary position with my legs straight out, but I feel that this is unadventurous, so I don't like to insist upon it.

'But while I do enjoy other positions, I find it almost impossible to climax in them. I don't know if this is mental or physical.'

Young marrieds with sex difficulties

The common time to get married is in the twenties. Alas, many young married women find that getting wed does *not* bring them orgasms! For instance, Jane (age twenty-three when she married) had had the occasional climax in her teens and early twenties. She thought that once she 'settled down', she would be having orgasms every night – but she was totally wrong.

You see, it's important to realise that many young couples need quite a lot of *time* to get accustomed to each other. It was actually two years before Jane started climaxing regularly with her husband. If you are a young married couple with orgasmic difficulties, it's often a very good idea to get some counselling from a doctor or a clinic specialising in sex matters.

Many young women in their twenties seek help from these sources. And frequently, problems that they thought were insurmountable can be defeated in quite a short space of time. Plenty of British, European and American couples go for counselling in their twenties. Wendy didn't.

She had a normal upbringing, and she started going out with a boy with a similar background to her own. But sexually the relationship was hopeless from the start, even though they loved each other and Wendy very much wanted to be married and to have children.

Like many women, she pushed her doubts about the relationship away and told herself all would be well after the wedding. After a few months she was practically screaming with frustration. She never got near an orgasm because when they made love her husband climaxed before even entering her.

Understandably he became demoralised and initiated sex less and less. Meanwhile Wendy had discovered her clitoris but couldn't persuade her husband to touch it. They didn't find it easy to discuss their problems, so they *avoided* talking about them. Neither of them spoke to anyone else either. As Wendy explained:

'I felt ashamed. I was quite attractive with a good job. I thought that everyone would assume that my marriage was marvellous. And I didn't want to own up that it wasn't.'

The couple never considered going for counselling.

Soon they were quarrelling and Wendy took to working late rather than face going home. Looking back, Wendy agrees that her marriage might have been saved if she and her husband had talked together, or agreed to go for professional help. Instead they divorced – two years after their wedding.

Young married women who have no orgasmic problems

Some women in their twenties are obviously and gloriously sexually compatible with their partners. Others can iron out any minor difficulties because they have a strong relationship and get on very well together.

Plenty of the twenty-somethings in our sample were doing just fine on the orgasm front without any outside or professional help. As one 23-year-old said: 'I've known my husband for over six years now – he was the first one for me and I was the first for him. I'm very happy because we've a wonderful sexual relationship where we both express our wishes and our dreams.'

This woman has several orgasms a week through love play and intercourse, and seems utterly content.

Another woman in her early twenties told us of a very uninhibited sex life resulting in as many orgasms a week as she could handle. She told us that she liked to masturbate in front of her husband. She also mentioned that oral sex combined with some fairly vigorous finger play gave her her most intense climaxes.

A 26-year-old who enjoys between eight and twelve orgasms a week says that being in love has made all the difference to her sex life. 'An orgasm means ten times more when you're madly in love. It's fireworks!' she says.

And a twenty-year-old in an apparently blissful relationship with her husband told us that she felt very lucky sexually and believed that her orgasmic ability was innate. But she went on to say that she felt that she and her partner were extremely sexually compatible. He is her first lover and they've now enjoyed nine months of 'sensational sex'. She added that she can reach orgasm without any direct genital stimulation and has climaxed during particularly good kissing! She describes these orgasms as less intense than genital ones, but she says it's nice to have the capacity to achieve them.

It's very nice for women like this twenty-year-old to be so naturally orgasmic, but it's important to say that *very* few twenty-plusses can have orgasms without a lot of direct stimulation.

Unmarried students and young professionals in their twenties

As a group these are the nearest to most people's vision of young fancy-free people having a whale of a time! We had some very frank input from a group of unmarried women students at a Scottish university. They were exceptionally bright young people and very willing to talk to each other and to us about the real nitty-gritty of sex and orgasms.

They said that they like to think that they can get away with anything at the present time and that they want to live life to the full. They also see themselves as being quite confident sexually, and when they want orgasms will go out and get them. They told us too that they try to withstand pressure from boyfriends – for example to have sex when they're not in the mood – and that they aren't scared to say what they feel.

'This also applies in bed,' said one 22-year-old. 'If a guy is not satisfying me, then I'll let him know. Sex can make or break a relationship.'

They also felt that respect was of paramount importance in a relationship and that if they didn't get it, they would move on.

They described themselves as 'in touch' with oral sex and masturbation and they all expected to have several orgasms a week one way or another. One particularly lusty student said that she often had two or three a day. If her partner wasn't around, these would be through masturbation.

Many of these young, intelligent women admitted that they had the best sex with their partners when they took control. So they favoured sex positions where the woman was on top. They felt that they could direct operations better that way and make sure that they got the clitoral stimulation they needed. They were very keen on oral sex, too, especially one student who regularly had fourteen orgasms a week.

We also found a lot of highly sexed young women among those just starting out on professional careers. Like the students, they were very clued up on contraception and were acutely aware of the danger of AIDS. So when they went out looking for sex, they practised it safely.

Many of the young twenty-something professionals felt that they had plenty of time yet to worry about settling down, so they tended to sleep with lots of different people. In this group we found a few women who would determinedly get their quota of orgasms, even if it meant having sex with someone they didn't particularly care for.

One young woman told us how she felt strangely attracted to a guy she actively disliked. She found it staggeringly easy to climax with him, and was convinced that this was because she wasn't wasting any time worrying about him and his feelings.

She felt that the way she was using him for her own pleasure was no different from how women had been treated through the centuries. In fact she claimed that she felt a little as if she was paying him back for what had happened to women through the ages and that this added to her excitement!

She was quite adamant that she would drop him when someone she could love came along, but that she saw no harm in enjoying as many orgasms as possible with this guy till then.

From our researches we should say that very, very few twenty-something women feel confident enough about their own sexuality and attraction to act in this way. And the vast majority wouldn't even want to. One young professional at twenty-six said that she thought people put too much emphasis on orgasms. She said that while she liked having orgasms with a partner, she had a much better success rate when she masturbated.

'I'm quite relaxed sexually,' she says, 'and when I'm with a man I don't feel under pressure to orgasm – I certainly don't feel a failure if I don't. But I can understand men being disappointed if I don't climax, because I would be worried if a man couldn't come with me.'

A 22-year-old who likes sex enormously told us that she was still finding having an orgasm a very hit or miss affair. She believes that worrying whether or not she's going to 'get there' very frequently stops her achieving her goal and leaves her teetering on the brink. Our survey showed that this is a very common problem in all age groups – though not as much in the over fifties.

Young mums

Many twenty-somethings have a miserable time sexually after the birth of their babies, but with help and support it's usually short-lived, though orgasms may be out of the question for a while. A lot of women told us that though they loved their husbands, they'd had virtually no sex drive since they'd given birth.

When they were pregnant, some of these mums had been having several orgasms every week, but they nearly all complained that after they were delivered it was as if someone had switched off both their ability to have orgasms and their desire for them as well. This situation often causes rows with young husbands and the couple have to find some compromise sexually if the marriage is to survive.

Fatigue is a major factor here and a terrible enemy of desire. But if a young woman can get enough rest and can accept that what she feels is just a horrid phase that *will* pass, she'll usually come through it quite quickly.

It's worse for women who weren't able to climax *before* having a baby, and, occasionally, their post-natal lack of interest will dent their sexual confidence so much that they'll give up trying for good.

A 23-year-old with two small children told us that sex had never given her much pleasure and now she hated it. In fact she'd decided that she wasn't going to bother with it at all in the future. She would occasionally let her husband have her, but she'd given up hoping for any orgasms herself. So much so that she'd be perfectly happy if she never had to have sex again.

Unfortunately, since this young woman's husband has quite a high sex drive, the omens aren't good for their marriage – especially since neither of them will agree to get help.

Asian twenty-somethings

One group of twenty-something females who face particular difficulties with orgasm are women of Indian or Pakistani ancestry, living in Western countries.

Many of them have been brought up in the West and have British, Australian, European or American friends. They may indeed also have benefited from some sex education at school. But within their own homes and communities they've usually been fiercely protected and have rarely been allowed the opportunity for sexual experimentation that most Western kids take for granted.

We spoke to a Hindu mother and counsellor who told us that before marriage the average Asian girl would be given absolutely no information about sex – and no ideas about orgasms.

What does seem to happen however is that as soon as a girl *is* married, she's welcomed into a network of married sisters, cousins and friends and the conversation in such groups can be quite explicit. So there is opportunity for learning about sex and orgasms *after* marriage, but not before.

Through talking to various counsellors and young Asian wives, we discovered that once married, these women often learn about climaxes very quickly. They've had a vague idea before marriage that there was a *duty* to respond sexually to their husbands, but once they're allowed to have sex, they quickly decide that they want orgasms and pleasure for *themselves*.

Although divorce is not quite as frowned on in the Asian community as it once was, there is still a lot of pressure on a woman to stay in her marriage, even if it's an unhappy one.

Mena's story is a good example of the difficulties faced by Asian women and their determination to overcome them. Mena was brought up in the West, where she's been well educated and now has a degree. At the age of twenty-three she entered into an arranged marriage with a man who was a distant relative and who had been brought up in India. This young man had masturbated as a lad, but had never been with a girl and had never even seen a woman naked.

Their wedding night was a disaster as neither of them knew where to put his penis, and he was so overwhelmed with nerves that he ejaculated as soon as he saw his bride undressed. Fortunately this couple had the sense to go for counselling where they learned to overcome their initial ignorance and anxiety. Life improved then.

Later they returned for more counselling as Mena wanted her young husband to learn more about stamina and other skills so that she could be sure of having orgasms. By the time they finished their second course of counselling they were very happy together and felt they were having very good sex.

So the twenties *can* be a happy time – if you work at it. Our survey shows that for many women this is a decade of burgeoning confidence both personally and sexually. It can also be a time of breathless romance and joy . . . and lots of lovely orgasms!

ORGASMS IN THE THIRTIES

You'd think that most women would build on their good experiences in their twenties, or learn from their bad ones and that the thirties would be the best decade so far. Well, it may be for some, but as we said in our survey, we noticed that many working women in this age group bemoaned the fact that their sex lives had gone to pot!

Some of these women had delayed having their first babies until their thirties because of their careers, and many of them had suffered, or were still suffering, from the post-natal sexual blues as described in our section on sex in the twenties.

In addition, most professional women told us that they felt that they were running just to remain on the spot, and that their sex lives had become casualties of their so-called 'successful' lifestyles.

The syndrome was the same when the husband was the career-minded partner.

In fact our researches suggest that the thirties are a very tough time, when people are juggling careers and mortgages and small children and child minders, and when time for love and sex is often squeezed to a minimum.

One 39-year-old told us that she often couldn't get in an orgasmic mood because she was far too stressed from work. 'So I haven't had a climax for six months,' she said rather sadly.

And a 36-year-old said: 'I cannot switch off thinking about

my work routine – I find it hard to do unnecessary things and I suppose sex is one of them!'

This woman also has a husband making his way up the career ladder and she says that finding time to sit and talk – let alone make love – is almost impossible. 'Sex is left to the last minute in bed when we should really be getting to sleep. It's a sad situation, but it's hard to make the effort to give more time for sex and relaxation.'

Another thirty-something woman with a hard-working husband told us about her sex life – or the lack of it:

'In the early stages of our relationship, our sex life was at its peak for a period of two years or so. But my orgasms faded away after the arrival of the children and because of all the work pressures on my husband.

'We'd like to have a more active sex life, but we never seem to find the time or energy. Instead we make do with a peck on the cheek, say goodnight, and roll on to our sleeping sides of the bed.

'On reflection I never imagined that after five and a half years our bedroom activity would be so dull and infrequent. No longer do we have orgasms seven times in a weekend – we probably only have that number spread over a few months!

'Pity really. Maybe I should make an effort tonight!'

A journalist on a top woman's magazine told us that her orgasmic life was more or less 'on hold'. 'I'm just so busy,' she said:

'At work I constantly worry about the kids and whether anyone's remembered to take them to the dentist or dancing lessons. Then at home I worry about all the deadlines in the office.

'Often sex is a disaster. It works, in a fashion, if my husband just goes ahead and fucks me. But if he really wants me to have orgasms, my mind is often incapable of switching off from work and into a kind of loving mode.

'I do love my husband and in some ways I'd love to get off the work treadmill and concentrate more on our life together. But we desperately need my money. I know loads of people like me. Sometimes it seems that everyone is either working far too hard because they're terrified of being made redundant, or they're out of work and depressed. There must be people in between, but I don't know any.

'So now I find having an orgasm with my husband almost impossible. But sometimes I feel really tense and charged up sexually and then, I'm ashamed to say, I masturbate in secret, quickly. It's a much more reliable way of getting sexual relief than bonking with the man I love.

But there are women in their thirties who have many of the stresses of the 'career girls' but without the financial gain or the potential to be a 'high-flyer'.

A 36-year-old who works on a supermarket check-out says that she is so tired at the end of the day that she literally *prays* that her husband won't want to have sex. He's been made redundant, so that she's the major breadwinner. But she is still coping with most of the household arrangements, so that switching instantly on to sex at the end of a hectic day isn't on. She says:

'I love my husband and there was a time when I adored orgasms. He used to call me "ever-ready" because I was always ready for climaxes. But all that's gone now. I'm constantly worried about money, the kids are at a demanding age and I can't get my mind round to sex at all. It's awful because my husband's a bit depressed at having lost his job, and sex is one of his real pleasures. Trouble is, I wish he'd have a cigarette instead. The only time I feel sexy is on holiday and we can't get away often because we can't afford it.'

Motherhood comes in for a lot of stick from thirty-something women who seem to have lost their orgasmic urges.

A 38-year-old who has hated her breasts ever since she had children told us that she castigates herself because she now takes too long to reach a climax. The changes in her body caused by childbirth have made her feel that she is an 'ugly' being who doesn't deserve orgasm.

Another 38-year-old describes herself as having switched off sexually since becoming a mother, and wishes she could switch back on again. She says:

'I was never sex-mad but since having children and combining that with a job, I really don't want sex. My husband always comes very quickly and I get nothing out of intercourse, except that I'm glad for him. It's a shame, because we used to be closer.'

We thought that this was a particularly sad situation since with medical advice this husband could probably be taught to 'last longer' – and the wife would therefore have a much better chance of reaching orgasm and rediscovering the joys of sex.

Very often women have successfully overcome tremendous obstacles to enjoying sex by the time they reach their thirties. But there are others who have a dark secret which they have been unable to share with anyone.

One such woman of thirty-nine told us how though she reached orgasm through masturbation at the early age of eleven, she had had a disastrous sex life. She said:

'Throughout childhood and adolescence I had very strong sexual urges, but when I became an adult and experienced the "real thing" it was all a terrible disappointment – though I think this could have been different if I'd had partners who were more sexually skilled.

'I really love my husband – he's my best friend. But our sex life is awful. He likes sex much more than I do but we only have it about once a month, which makes me feel very sorry for him.'

She then went on to say that she had been raped at the age of twenty-one and had never spoken to anyone about it. Unfortunately we've had no way of getting in touch with this particular lady, but we would urge her or anyone in her situation to get in touch with the nearest Rape Crisis Centre.

Even if the rape took place ages ago, the centre will help deal with the terrors of the past so that the victim can begin to look forward to a more positive sex life in the future.

Although the thirties do seem to be such a troublesome time for so many, there are still plenty of women in this age group who are having a golden sex life, with lots of fun and orgasms between the sheets.

A 36-year-old said that after having each of her three children she's got progressively more orgasmic. Now she can have multiple orgasms and she says that with every passing year she gets raunchier.

'I feel like having sex more and more,' she says, 'much to my partner's delight!'

Another 36-year-old confided that she had increased her tally of orgasms dramatically in the last seven years. Her only complaint was that she has never so far managed to climax during intercourse without stimulation. 'I'd like to,' she said. 'I suppose I read too much D.H. Lawrence when I was young!'

On a slightly different tack, a thirty-year-old who has what she describes as a wonderful sex life, wanted us to record the fact that she and her man invariably have simultaneous orgasms. She says that when she was a virgin she assumed that coming together would be the norm and would happen automatically. As an adult she found climaxing during intercourse quite hard, but once she got the hang of it, orgasms happened easily – and simultaneously with the partner's.

In the three long-term relationships she's had, she has always found that she could climax with her man. She says:

'I have been with my current partner for ten years and we always come together quite naturally, whatever we're doing. Yet we're always reading that this is terribly difficult to achieve. We hope that the *Big O* book will put things right and indicate how common it really is for men and women to come together.'

Well, we've put her point of view and are delighted that her orgasmic pattern fits her partner so well. But we feel bound to point out that in our survey we found only 2 per cent of women always synchronised with their partner, while about 60 per cent said they came simultaneously with their partner 'some of the time'.

In summary, we reckon that a lot of women in their thirties do seem to be in control of their sex lives, even though so many of them are suffering from the stresses and strains of modern life. Though less than half of the women we surveyed in this age group said that they could orgasm whenever they wanted, about two-thirds of them regularly had multiple orgasms and the *majority* of them said that they enjoyed good sex lives!

The thirty-somethings enjoy quite a repertoire of sexual positions, but those where the woman is *on top* came out favourite. Finally, in this age group a lot of women begin to notice that their sex drives vary at different points of the month.

The commonest time for feeling sexy is just before a period, though many women said that their raunchiest time was mid-cycle – and a few claimed to be really hot stuff during the period itself.

ORGASMS IN THE FORTIES

The reward for getting through the tiring and turbulent thirties is the fulfilling forties!

The vast majority of forty-something women in our survey had sorted out their jobs or careers, put their relationships in order – changed them where necessary – and were progressing onward and upward with their lives. . . *And* they were having masses of orgasms. Two-thirds of this age group knew they had specially sexy times of the month and for many of them it coincided with the few days just before their periods.

As a group they enjoyed multiple orgasms much more frequently than any of the younger age groups, but it's important to note that even with all their confidence and skill, *less than half* of these women felt that they could climax every time they wanted to.

Although this age group is pretty sexually active, not everyone was swinging from the chandeliers twice nightly. One forty-year-old felt very down about her sex life. She'd had several lovers in her time and none of them had ever given her what she called a good orgasm. She said that only a vibrator could do that, but that she didn't have one at the moment.

She is in a long-term relationship and sometimes considers opting out of it, but never quite gets round to it. She loves her partner, but feels that he never gives her enough petting in bed so she never comes with him. Sometimes she hankers for something better, but mostly she feels she might as well settle for what she has.

Another woman told us that filling in our survey had made her see that she must get out of her present relationship as the only satisfaction she ever got sexually was through masturbation, and the rest of the marriage was dire as well.

Then a 43-year-old said that she no longer loved her

partner and had definite plans to move on. But she'd been surprised that since she admitted to herself that the relationship was fatally flawed, she'd started having orgasms during intercourse on a regular basis, which she'd never been able to do before.

She said, 'I started to be more selfish about my own needs and worry less about my performance. But now I yearn to feel what it would be like with someone I feel passionately for simply because I have this new knowledge and ability.'

Another 43-year-old who has had a hysterectomy remarked that sex was much better for her now than it had been before the operation. But she said that her body and mind are not always 'in sync'. She finds that orgasm is deeply enjoyable when she makes the effort, but admits that she can't always be bothered.

Fatigue rears its ugly head in many forty-something women's answers, just as it did among the thirty-somethings. It's worth saying here that when one of us (C.W.) interviewed the world-famous sex expert Dr Ruth Westheimer, she said that fatigue had become the biggest sex problem for women world-wide.

Out of the women we surveyed who claimed to have wonderful sex lives, a high proportion were no longer with their original marriage (or long-term) partner. Several of these women described miserable experiences in previous relationships. One said that she used to cry herself to sleep with frustration. And several remembered awful times when they'd laid awake and masturbated next to their post-coital husbands.

This is common. In our survey 15 per cent of respondents said they'd done it! It sounds as if many women become quite adept at matching their movements to their man's snores and grunts, and holding their breath as he turns over. Other women get up out of their warm bed and masturbate in silent fury in the bathroom.

On the brighter side, a 47-year-old told us that she only has occasional sex with her new man as he lives abroad. But she says, 'I'm much happier having good sex once every six months than the awful sex I had during a twelve-year marriage. Bad sex can be a very destructive thing.'

An executive of forty-three described how being married to a womaniser had made her feel used and desperately unhappy. She says, 'I never enjoyed sex until I met my second husband. I feel so well loved now that it's almost like being a different person. Being in a stable, loving, caring relationship definitely helps achieve orgasms.'

However, not all women who have changed their original partner have switched to another *man*. And while this book is essentially for heterosexual couples, it's only fair to record the fact that several forty-something women told us that they had chosen lesbian relationships. Some of them made the point that a woman usually understands what another woman wants in bed, and so can supply the right caresses.

A 48-year-old confessed to several sexual involvements with women. She felt that orgasms with females could be very exciting and that 'somehow they lasted longer'. Was this true? Or was it just that the thrill of a 'forbidden' relationship made the climax seem to last and last? We do not know. She has stayed married through several lesbian affairs and says that her husband loves her and knows she loves him. Also they enjoy having sex together, so they don't see her other occasional activities as a problem.

Finally let us not forget that in this age group not every woman that we spoke to had a partner. Some women had come out of bad marriages and had not yet found new 'boyfriends' to their taste. But several of these women were highly sexed and enjoyed masturbating on a regular basis. One of our correspondents regularly clocks up thirty orgasms a week.

Another who masturbates frequently to exciting fantasies says that 'you meet a better class of person that way!'

The forties is a time of consolidation and enjoyment. We

felt the vast majority of the forty-somethings who we surveyed were optimistic, lively and sexy women. And as one of them said: 'If you can have good orgasms and plenty of them, you don't worry so much about your crows' feet and laughter lines!'

ORGASMS IN THE FIFTIES

The picture of women in their fifties is not unlike that in the forties, but in most women's cases their children have now left home and may be settled with partners of their own, which gives mum more freedom and the opportunity to enjoy herself.

One 53-year-old makes sure that she and her husband, who both work full time, always keep Saturday or Sunday afternoons completely free so that they can make love. They've been married for more than twenty-five years and she says that sometimes they have very passionate sex with lots of orgasms while at other times it's just very pleasant. But she says that it's vital for people to organise time to be with each other *when they're young*. Otherwise, she says, they often grow apart so that when they finally have the house to themselves, they have nothing to say to each other and no wish to give each other orgasms.

Another long-term married woman with thirty-six years of wedded bliss behind her said: 'As we near sixty, we seem to have the same sort of needs and I am so glad to have a regular lover who gives me satisfaction. It might not even be too late to get rid of some of my hang-ups.'

After the menopause

Most women in their fifties have passed through the menopause. The drop in female hormones which occurs at this time can interfere with your ability to have orgasms. For a start, the fall in hormone levels will very likely cause *vaginal dryness*. Of course women of other ages can suffer from this, too, but not to the same extent. After the menopause, the usual lubricating creams and liquids that so many women use may not be sufficient.

Happily, for many women hormone replacement vaginal cream will put things right.

However, it is also a good idea to pour a lubricant (such as Astroglide or Senselle) over the clitoris, in order to make orgasm easier. All the tissues seem to be less lubricated around this time and clitoral stimulation without any added lubrication can sometimes be uncomfortable and lead women to fear they might damage themselves. Some also worry that they've lost the knack of reaching a climax.

Of course, many women are put on HRT to combat hot flushes and other menopause and post-menopause symptoms. And a growing number of women who like sex are asking for HRT even if their symptoms are not severe simply because they've been told that it will help their love lives! Is this a good idea? It's something you should talk over with your own doctor before embarking on it . . .

Many women remember that when they went on the Pill for the first time, they had to try several different types before they found one that suited them. HRT is much the same and it can take a while before a woman feels she's found the right preparation. In fact, Dr Miriam Stoppard, the well-known TV broadcaster and medical writer, told us that even she had to try three or four different types of HRT (and also to change her specialist!) before she was happy with what she was being prescribed.

Many women who find that they *are* suited to HRT say that their sex lives improve. One 52-year-old described this as a great bonus! And a 57-year-old told us how she had a relationship after going on HRT which gave her 'the best sex of my life'.

She said that prior to the menopause she had noticed that she was a bit dry. But once she was on HRT she said that moisture was *not* a problem – in fact, she had more than enough.

HRT hasn't always been with us, yet there have always been women who have remained sexually active well into their later years. One woman told us how she'd discovered that her grandparents still made love and obviously enjoyed it. She was fifteen at the time and they were well into their fifties. 'This was a powerful and positive sexual message for me,' she says. 'I was terribly pleased about it and now I'm in my fifties too, I hope that I'll be able to keep going and enjoy it as long as they did.'

For some fifty-somethings however, their sex lives are curtailed because of their husbands' infirmity. A 58-year-old explained how she often faked orgasm, even though she would have liked to have one or more climaxes, just to get intercourse over with – as her husband suffered from a severe back problem which gave him terrible cramps.

'I'm blessed with a wonderful, attentive husband who does his very best to make me happy, both sexually and otherwise. But I can't help wishing that we could return to the days before his illness.'

Finally, as with the forty-plusses, masturbation is on the menu for today's highly-sexed fifty-something woman who finds herself without a partner.

A woman of fifty-seven who told us that she's had brilliant sex at different times in her life explained that she was having the most intense orgasms of her life *now* without a man. She's using a massager instead of a conventional vibrator and is regularly having five orgasms per session.

'Could a man keep up with me?' she asks.

ORGASMS IN THE SIXTIES AND BEYOND

Let's say at the outset of this section that many women of 'a certain age' feel that they can live perfectly well without sex. Maybe they never enjoyed it much. Perhaps they've had a lot of gynaecological trouble and are unable to regard their genitals as instruments of pleasure.

We think it's important that these women should be allowed to make their own choice. Of course, the only problem arises when they are married to men who still want sex on a regular basis. But nowadays a woman who's fit and still keen on sex is not likely to abandon her love life just because she qualifies for a free bus pass! Women in this age group don't talk about sex nearly as much as younger women – they were brought up differently. But there is no doubt that many in their sixties and seventies are having sex, and continuing to enjoy powerful orgasms.

We frequently receive letters from quite elderly people confessing that after the death of their partner what they miss most is sex. And we know of many women in their seventies who have been for counselling in a bid to have good orgasms with new partners.

People in their 'third age' tell us that sex can be just as rewarding and intense, but that it's not as hurried. 'We're retired and we've been married for almost fifty years, so we're not in a rush,' said one lady of seventy-six, 'and we can take all afternoon over something that used to be over and done with in twenty minutes!'

And speaking to a warden in a block of old-people's flats, we learned that retired and widowed people quite often fall for new partners and that there's no doubt that these relationships are usually sexual.

Good luck to them, we say. And isn't it great to know that we can still look forward to oodles of sex in our sixties, seventies and beyond?

AS WOMEN GET MORE ORGASMIC, MEN GET *LESS*!

As we've hinted in some of our previous sections in this chapter, some women begin to have problems in their sexual relationship as they get older – because their men simply can't keep up with them. The same women often remember a time in their teens or twenties when the man was climaxing all over the place, while *they* couldn't quite get there.

Well, men peak early. But as this book demonstrates, women peak late! And as women get older, they are more and more likely to be able to rely on having good orgasms. It seems ironic then that just at the point where women can trip off as many orgasms as they like, their man's strike rate may drop off dramatically.

The average man probably has around four orgasms a week. But once he's into his sixties, he's lucky if he can manage just one orgasm per week. This is at a time when some fit, sexy sixty-year-old women have four or five orgasms in one session alone! So this is one hell of a disparity.

Most couples solve this difference by concentrating on *quality* sex, rather than quantity. And a caring, sympathetic husband can bring his wife to as many orgasms as she wants by means of his tongue or his fingers. Sometimes they can have intercourse for a while, even if he's not going to be able to go all the way to a climax. This can be satisfying for both of them, even if his erection may not be as reliable as it once was.

Also, they can turn sex into a special occasion on the days when he has the energy to climax. As we've mentioned already, some men develop health problems and some of these, arthritis for example, can lead to difficulties when it comes to finger-play.

So more and more couples of retirement age are buying vibrators, which are not only useful in giving their partners orgasms, but can also be a wonderful help in boosting a man's flagging erection.

SOLO ORGASM IN THE LATER YEARS

We've seen that masturbation is one form of sex used by most women at some time – and that it's often the most reliable way for a woman to have an orgasm. For some people it's the most intense way, too.

And in the forties and fifties masturbation is very commonly practised by women who are without partners – either temporarily or permanently. In later life, many women worry that masturbation might be bad for them. This may be due to the moral climate in which they grew up, or it may be caused by natural worries about health and strength in retirement.

We can tell you that masturbation is not harmful. Furthermore, we think it's a healthy thing to do. It provides people with pleasure and relaxation, and it is an entirely safe activity. For women of all ages and not least those in later life, masturbation can provide wonderful release from tension. It can also help to cure headaches and insomnia, say many women. It can evoke a marvellous sense of well-being – and it's very, very nice.

However, with the passing years, the whole genital area becomes less moist than it once was. For that reason we recommend the use of some kind of emollient, or better still the use of one of the products designed for this particular job, like K-Y Jelly or Senselle – or (in the USA) Astroglide.

A few drops of liquid on the clitoris can enhance pleasure immediately and will prevent those delicate tissues from feeling stretched or irritated. You can use saliva, of course, but it does tend to dry up rather quickly.

There are no limits to the number of orgasms a woman in later life can enjoy if she is in good health. So enjoy.

5

WHAT ORGASMS FEEL LIKE TO WOMEN

Female Orgasms Are Not All the Same • Orgasms Vary From Woman to Woman • Different Orgasms For Different Occasions • Love Play *Versus* Intercourse Orgasms • Masturbation Orgasms • How Mood, the Setting and the Man Can Affect the Way You Feel about Orgasms • What Women Say about Orgasm

FEMALE ORGASMS ARE *NOT* ALL THE SAME!

It's easy to assume that all female orgasms are much the same. Men, in particular, tend to take a rather stereotypical view of feminine climaxes – mostly based on what they learned from their friends as youngsters. ('You push your middle finger in and out, and then they shriek. That's about it, really.')

In actual fact, women's orgasms vary enormously in power and emotional depth. Sometimes they're quite minor events, which scarcely ruffle the lady's hair. On other occasions, a climax can be so shattering that the woman will remember it for the rest of her life.

So in this chapter, we shall see just how variable the feelings of climax really are.

ORGASMS VARY FROM WOMAN TO WOMAN

When we asked women up and down the country to describe an orgasm, some women gave a one word answer: 'nice', 'joyful' or 'wicked'! Others wrote *pages* of X-rated prose.

Now it may be that the one-word brigade have orgasms that are just as wonderful as the more expansive lot; indeed it's possible that some of our correspondents were so busy *having* orgasms that they didn't want to waste time writing about them.

But it's certainly true that women have varying experiences, and that orgasm is of vital importance to some, but nothing to get steamed up about for others. The important thing is that each woman should feel happy and satisfied with her own climaxes irrespective of what she suspects other women are up to.

Some of our correspondents complained to us that their

partners often undermined their feelings about themselves by comparing them with other lovers they'd had.

Thirty-three-year-old Amanda told us that she has marvellous orgasms with her man, but he's unconvinced she's having a good time, because his ex-wife used to shriek and to wet herself as she came, and Amanda doesn't.

'He keeps asking me rather sorrowfully if I'm sure I'm "getting there",' said Amanda:

> 'This is usually when I'm lying in an exhausted heap having just come! I've tried screaming and shouting at the appropriate moment, but it just feels false for me. I enjoy orgasms but I'm a quiet kind of person. The trouble is that if my boyfriend can't learn to accept that his ex and I are just different, then I'm probably going to kill him, or walk out – or both!'

It's also worth remembering that women who only have a few orgasms a month may well be just as happy and satisfied as the ones who have thirty climaxes a week. Most men with a bit of experience enjoy the fact that women vary a lot. As one said to us: 'Yes, every woman is different, but they're all *very* nice.'

DIFFERENT ORGASMS FOR DIFFERENT OCCASIONS

'If I'm not in the mood,' said one 35-year-old in our survey, 'it wouldn't matter if he humped me all night, I *still* wouldn't have an orgasm.'

Most other women felt the same way. A 47-year-old who has masses of orgasms drew us this picture (Fig. 5.1 on page 130) to show us how different her orgasms felt on different days. We saw in Chapter Four that many women feel sexier at different times of their monthly cycles.

Clever women work this knowledge to their advantage. One told us how she planned romantic breaks for her and her husband when she knew she'd be feeling raunchy.

A single 28-year-old who told us it was her misfortune to love a married man, said that since they weren't able to spend many nights together, she tried to ensure that these coincided with her most orgasmic times. But not all women have managed to work out a pattern for their orgasms. And some have told us that they feel quite bewildered that one day they'll climax with the merest touch of the clitoris while at other times no amount of clitoral attention does the trick. Worse than that, some days it actually turns them right off.

We do urge women like this to have a go at keeping a 'desire diary' over several months, because if they can learn to predict their sexual moods, it can make life much easier.

Forty-two-year-old Sarah told us that she'd finally worked out that she felt at her sexiest halfway through her cycle, and then again immediately after her period. 'Knowing this fact has helped my marriage. At least when I'm *not* in the mood, my poor husband has some idea when I'm going to be begging for orgasms again!'

Another forty-something said that she'd developed a few tricks to help her on those 'off days'. By flexing the muscles in her tummy, legs and genitals, she could make herself more excited, and generally reach orgasm if she wanted to.

She said, 'Even if I'm not in the mood, I may well come, and then feel marvellously relaxed and relieved afterwards.'

If you're a man, the important thing to realise is that even if what you did to a woman on Monday to bring her to orgasm was wildly successful, it may not work on Tuesday. Trying something else may do the trick.

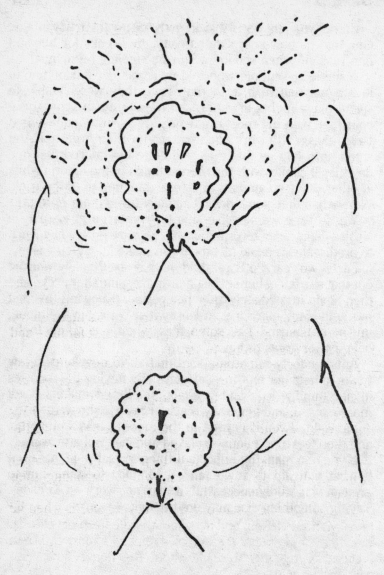

Fig. 5.1

LOVE PLAY *VERSUS* INTERCOURSE ORGASMS

Our survey shows that six out of ten women say that love play orgasms are best for them, while other women prefer those achieved during sexual intercourse. So once again, females do vary a lot.

Many women told us that if they were to have deep and earth-shattering climaxes, they had to have their man's penis inside them. They often liked, or needed clitoral stimulation, too, but it was the union with the partner and the feeling of him deep inside them that gave them their satisfaction.

Other women have explained to us how they *never* have orgasms during intercourse, even with clitoral stimulation. Many swear by oral sex as the most reliable method of 'getting there'. Others like a lot of rubbing of the clitoris. Glenda, aged thirty-six, said: 'Nothing beats the uncomplicated, focused orgasm I get from having my partner rub my clitoris. Other things are fine, but that's the best for me – and the feelings nearly lift my head off.'

Another group of women also prefer orgasms through love play but say that they need a two-pronged approach. What they love is to have their man put a finger inside them and move it swiftly in and out while at the same time rubbing the clitoris with the other hand. Other women like to do the rubbing themselves while their man attends to their vagina.

And some ladies like the man to put a lubricated finger from one hand up their bottom, while stimulating their genitals with the other hand.

'What's best of all,' said one frank 42-year-old, 'is when he looks after my bottom and my vagina, while I rub my clitoris. I feel that I'm being possessed all over, and I adore it. When I come in this way, I really shout the house down. It's fantastic!'

So, there doesn't seem to be a straightforward answer to

the question of whether orgasms are stronger or better through intercourse, or through love play, because women's tastes vary so much. These tastes may also change with the passing years.

A good lover will learn what makes his partner have orgasms most easily and *try* to keep pace with what she wants at different times.

MASTURBATION ORGASMS

The great majority of the women who filled in our survey – 70 per cent of them – told us that they masturbate. So it is no surprise to learn that many females feel that masturbation is the most *reliable* route to orgasm.

'When I'm with my partner,' said a 24-year old, 'I sometimes feel as if my clitoris is jumping about all over the place. He encourages me to place his fingers exactly where I want to be stroked – and I do. But within seconds the bit I need to be touched seems to have moved. It's not my boyfriend's fault. He tries ever so hard. But it drives me mad.'

And a 30-year-old woman bemoaned the fact that her man could labour long and hard on her pink bits – to no avail. But if she faked an orgasm and later went out to the bathroom and masturbated, she could come in less than a minute.

In Chapter Four we saw how a high-powered career woman preferred to masturbate quickly when she needed relief, rather than spend time getting into the mood for full sex with her husband. And a computer expert, who regularly speaks at top business conferences, told us that when she feels nervous before a speech, having an orgasm through masturbation is the only thing that keeps her on an even keel.

Recently she was pacing up and down backstage in a conference centre before giving her presentation. 'I felt I

MUST have an orgasm,' she said, 'so I retired to the dressing room and had eight! They were really intense and I felt marvellous. I think I could have gone on and on if I hadn't had to go on stage!'

Women who masturbate regularly say that a DIY orgasm can feel like a sigh or a gentle sneeze: a moment of soothing comfort and nothing more. But at other times, it can be so powerful that the spasms of ecstasy seem to go on and on.

Of course, as we saw in Chapter Three, *first* orgasms through masturbation can be mind-blowing, but some women say that that intensity is rarely repeated. However, Monica, a UK teacher, says that for her masturbation is *always* the most powerful kind of orgasm. 'It knocks me sideways,' she says. 'But don't print my full name – I'm sure people don't think that teachers should have huge orgasms!'

Monica wasn't the only woman who found masturbation the most powerful way to get relief. Twelve per cent of women in our survey said that they get most of their climaxes this way, and many of those told us that no other orgasms could match the strength of the ones achieved through masturbation.

When it came to the technique of masturbation, many women were happy with clitoral stimulation either by hand or with a vibrator. But some ladies told us that they needed to feel something in the vagina, too.

Susie said: 'I *can* have an orgasm just by stroking my clitoris, but it doesn't feel that great. However, if I put three fingers into my vagina, while I'm rubbing my clitoris with my right hand, I usually have a very intense climax – it's lovely!'

But don't let's forget that there are women who have terrible hang-ups about masturbation – they feel that it's wrong or unnatural. This is usually as a result of an over-strict upbringing. Incidentally, it is possible to lose these bad feelings with the help of an understanding partner, or through therapy.

Most women's feelings are extremely positive about

masturbation. They regard it as a delicious dish on a varied menu. They may not eat it every day, but they're happy to select it on a regular basis!

HOW MOOD, THE SETTING AND THE MAN CAN AFFECT THE WAY YOU FEEL ABOUT ORGASMS

Many things can affect a woman's ability to reach orgasm – and the way it feels when she has it. For example, illness, overwork and stress can play havoc with your orgasms. And matters will not improve until you deal with the *cause* of the problem. But there are three factors which are particularly likely to affect your climaxes:

- your mood;
- the setting;
- the man.

Your mood

We've seen already how feeling that you're not in the right mood for an orgasm can ensure that you don't have one. Some women told us that the *slightest* irritant sent them back to square one, even if they were on the right path for a climax. It could be the wrong music playing on the radio, for example, or a news programme starting up on the television.

'News programmes are *not* conducive to letting yourself go and having climaxes,' said Emma. 'You find yourself concentrating on all that interminable political stuff, or you get emotional about the plight of children in a war zone, or something. Once your mind's gone over to that, your mood totally changes and orgasm is impossible.'

As we've said at the beginning of this section, major personal problems can prevent women having orgasms, and if there's a serious flaw in a relationship, a woman's mood may be so badly affected that she can't dredge up an orgasm to save her life. But it's important for her to realise that it's not her orgasmic ability that's gone wrong, it's her marriage or partnership, and *that's* what she needs to sort out.

Sometimes there are temporary blips in relationships that can actually catapult a woman into the mood for orgasms and *more* orgasms. Thirty-seven-year-old Mary explained how she had felt incredibly raunchy when she suspected her husband of having an affair:

'We'd been together for fifteen years and sex had become rather routine, I'm afraid. Suddenly I saw him in a fresh light and I kept imagining him with this younger girl. It was like an aphrodisiac – I couldn't get enough of him. I was angry but I was incredibly fired up sexually, too.

'It turned out later that he *had* been very interested in that girl, but they hadn't *quite* got to bed. Fortunately, my passionate moods made my husband feel great and probably saved my marriage. I still remember those orgasms. They rocked my whole body and I just kept having them.'

Another woman – we'll call her Brenda – wrote to say that she just couldn't climax during a difficult time in her marriage. Her husband had left her for a new partner, but had quickly returned to her, vowing eternal love:

'When he came back he was in a very emotional state. I wanted to help him, but felt numb inside. And those feelings that normally flow and turn into an orgasm had gone dead. Thankfully, we stuck at it, and as I realised he was home to stay and that I could trust him, my sensations thawed out. And now I'm having plenty of orgasms again – thank goodness.'

Often the *best* mood for sex and orgasms is one which a woman deliberately thinks herself into. If she can keep conjuring up sexy mental pictures throughout the day, her mind will be halfway to orgasm by the time she sees her partner in the evening.

Several women we spoke to told us how generating a raunchy mood through the day helped them to have orgasms later on. 'Though my husband is a workaholic,' said one 29-year-old, 'I'm sure he thinks of sex several times in every hour through the day. This used to mean that he was raring to go sexually as soon as he got home, while my mind was full of other things. Now I try to create the right mood on the days I fancy having sex and it's like having foreplay for hours before we meet up. It definitely helps.'

Many women felt at their sexiest on holiday because they felt they could justifiably relax and let themselves go.

'At home,' said one busy 40-year-old, 'I can't seem to give myself permission to switch off worrying about day-to-day things and this completely ruins the mood. On holiday I stop worrying and I practically have orgasms coming out of my ears.'

One woman said that she really resented it if her husband made a move towards her when she felt she was giving out signals that she wasn't interested.

'I feel pressurised and quite angry – and as if he's just one more thing to fit into my crowded day.'

Her sentiment was echoed by many of the women we surveyed, though a 46-year-old did admit that occasionally when she *thought* she wasn't in the mood, her resistance was overcome and she ended up having a marvellous orgasm.

'I suppose it's very female to change your mind – but that's what I am after all!'

Several women said that they felt very rejected if they had busied themselves creating a sexy mood at home, only to have it dashed by husbands who turned up their noses at special culinary surprises. Or worse still, the male partner may want to watch some important football match on TV just when the wife has prepared a candlelit dinner – with sex as the dessert! As one fairly bitter correspondent said: 'Women are *always* giving their husbands sex on days when they don't feel in the mood at all. But if a *man* isn't in the mood, a wife may as well forget it, or see to herself in private.'

However, on a more positive note, we were delighted to find that the majority of women in long-term relationships who filled in our survey seemed to feel that they were in tune with their regular partners and able to communicate their own moods and desires successfully.

The setting

Holidays crop up again here. It's quite amazing how many busy women feel that they need trips away to beautiful places in order to enjoy really good orgasms.

'Getting away definitely helps me,' said Claire. 'When we arrive at our destination, we usually walk around the place together arm in arm. Then we have a coffee or a drink and go to bed. I invariably have a marvellous orgasm. It's not just that I've relaxed; it's also the different sights, and the sounds and smells drifting into our open window.'

Because atmosphere and setting are so important to women, it's vital that they create the right ambience in their love-making location. For example, it's hard to relax and let yourself go if your bedroom is cold. Oral sex, in particular, is a no-no unless you're warm all over.

Women complain too that their bedroom often has to double as a male storeroom!

'We've got stacks of his old railway magazines in every corner of our bedroom,' said one long-suffering 54-year-old. 'I find this very depressing and unromantic.'

Another woman told us of her affair with a confirmed bachelor. 'Every time I went to see him, he seemed to have just come back from the laundry and his underwear was drying on radiators all round his flat. Once, at a critical moment, I opened my eyes and saw six pairs of horrible old damp Y-fronts arranged not three feet from his bed. I had been feeling quite passionate but I just thought, "What price romance?" and gave up.'

Several women in our survey mentioned the great outdoors when it came to spicing up their love-making and finding suitable settings for orgasms. A thirty-year-old told us that she and her man frequently go out for walks by the river, and if they can find a quiet nook, they have sex.

'I rarely actually quite "come" on these excursions,' she said, 'but I feel terrifically sexy, and by the time we get home, I'm tearing my bloke's clothes off. I always end up having several orgasms.'

One lusty 47-year-old told of a day etched in her memory where she and her husband made love in a steamed-up car beside a rugby pitch where the local team was training.

'I wonder if they saw the car rocking,' she said. 'I had one of the best orgasms of my life in that setting. It was six years ago and I still remember every detail.'

Another woman confessed to having orgasms in the cinema. 'My husband and I own a little shop which we close on Wednesday afternoons. Some weeks we go to a film on our day off, just after lunch, when the cinema is quiet. We have a kiss and cuddle and my husband fingers me till I come. I have to stifle my usual cries, but I love it and I'm always ready for more orgasms when we get home.'

We can't leave this section without mentioning two important factors:

1. It's no good finding the perfect setting for the orgasm of a life-time, if you don't allocate plenty of TIME for it.
2. Children rapidly ruin your perfect setting. So beg, borrow or steal a babysitter. Better still, persuade granny to have the kids while you and your man take a romantic break away.

The man

Although some women in our survey told us of raunchy sex
with strangers, or with men they didn't like very much, the
predominant message that came over to us from our
correspondents was that most women wanted their orgasms
with men that they loved.

Obviously they were put off by excessively jealous men,
violent men, mean men and men who didn't consider their
needs. But many women stayed with blokes who were far
from perfect, because they loved them. Occasionally women
told us how they'd met men who seemed ideal, but who just
weren't right for them, no matter how they tried.

Veronica, a divorcée of thirty-four told us how she met a
wonderful, handsome, wealthy, cultured man who fell in love
with her after a few dates. Yet she couldn't face orgasm with
him:

He was so charming and all my girlfriends thought he
was marvellous, but something was wrong.

'Things came to a head when he invited me to Vienna
for a long weekend. I'd never been there and longed to
go, but I realised that he would expect me to have sex
with him, which so far I'd avoided. I knew I would never
be able to come with him because I just didn't like the
feel or smell of his skin, and nothing I did could alter
those feelings about him as a man. Perhaps I should
have gone to Vienna and then pretended I had a
headache, but I couldn't have done that to him. He was
too nice.

'I've had quite a number of lovers in my life and never
felt that I couldn't orgasm with any of the rest of them.
It was just chemistry, I suppose, and if it's not right
there's nothing on earth you can do to change it.'

On a happier note, plenty of women in our survey were
extremely complimentary about their men and very happy

and comfortable with them. They knew that they had healthy
love-lives with their fair share of orgasms and they were very
grateful. In fact, many women told us that they couldn't
envision having anything like as good a sex life with anyone
else. A widow paid a touching tribute to her late husband and
the sex life they'd shared:

> 'I have orgasms on my own now Bill has gone. The
> orgasms help me to relax and often help conjure up a
> memory of the ones I shared with him. I enjoy them
> and am pleased to still be able to enjoy these excited
> feelings.
>
> 'But orgasms on my own can never compare to the
> wonderful times I had when Bill was alive. We laughed
> so much together and my orgasms were a triumph for
> both of us. Sex on its own is OK – but sex with the right
> man is in a totally different class.'

WHAT WOMEN SAY ABOUT ORGASM

Our survey asked women to describe their feelings at the
moment of orgasm. The vast majority of those who answered
were marvellously poetic and some were so 'hot' we almost
had to rush off and take a cold shower!

A small group of our correspondents told us that their
pleasure at the moment of orgasm was so incredibly
powerful that it frequently melded into pain.

'It can be such an intense feeling that it's almost
unbearable and unpleasant,' said 39-year-old Lynne. 'I get a
stomach ache afterwards, which is why I don't allow myself
to have them too often. At other times my orgasms can be
sweet and relaxing, but they're not as intense.'

Another woman who experiences pain is Caroline. 'It
doesn't always happen,' she said, 'but sometimes when I
have a really shattering climax I immediately get a terrible

spasm in my bottom. It's desperately painful and no matter what I try, I can't get rid of it for ages. Thank God it doesn't happen often or it might put me off having orgasms, which would be unthinkable – I like to have at least six every week.'

Moira, a woman of fifty-seven, told us that she's always enjoyed deep orgasms with a sensation of a lot of vaginal contractions. Recently, though, she's felt real pain during these contractions and it's so bad she's avoiding having sex.

Moira's clearly not alone. According to Masters and Johnson, many mature women develop cramping pains in their wombs during orgasm. Fortunately M and J say that these can be alleviated by hormone therapy.

And while we're still on the subject of pain, we were intrigued by Cassie who described her orgasms as 'like labour!'

Some women suffered no physical pain, but found that their orgasms tended to leave them very emotional and weepy.

'I cry afterwards,' said 38-year-old Elizabeth.

While Annie, a 44-year-old with a terrific appetite for sex, told us:

'There is a distinct feeling of rising to a climax which pulsates through my body. I feel my genital muscles contract and relax which sends waves of intense pleasure through my frame. Afterwards there's a tremendous sense of release, often culminating in an emotional outburst with lots of tears.'

About half the women who wrote to us described their orgasms in physical terms – the bits that tingled and so on. Here are a few examples:

'A rush of spasms with pins-and-needles feelings in my legs.'

A 32-year-old who has at least three orgasms every week said:

'It starts as a lovely tickly sensation in and around the

vagina and on the clitoris. It becomes more and more intense, spreading throughout my body till there's no room for anything else. Then it subsides the same way as it came. It usually lasts ten seconds or so and is absolute bliss!'

Nina, a 20-year-old who described herself as highly orgasmic, explained that during her climax:

'Everything feels sensitised, especially tummy, breasts and vagina. I have intense vaginal contractions. It's like I'm on fire and then being blown out. My first and third orgasms are more powerful then my second one.'

And Sheena, who's 22, said: 'It's an intense tingling which spreads violently and pleasurably throughout my whole body and down to my toes.'

A teenager who has been having sex for three years told us that: 'My feet and legs go quivery and shake. Then my head spins and goes dizzy while my vagina contracts very quickly and my whole body then goes numb. Sometimes my face really tingles.'

Another twenty-something said: 'It's the most over-whelming, intense, concentrated physical pleasure I've ever experienced. It becomes so physically intense, it almost numbs my body. It's probably the ultimate physical pleasure.'

Several women told us that orgasm made them feel as if they were going to faint, while Pat said that she always knew very early on in love-making if she was going to 'get there' or not:

'There's this sudden moment when I know it's inevitable. I get tightness and pressure building up round my vulva and then it releases in great waves throughout my body. My body then twitches and has several mini-orgasms after the big one.'

And Carla, a student who often has three climaxes in a day explained:

'As I approach orgasm, my whole body is tense, then as I come, it's like a load of nerves and feelings releasing themselves. You can't believe your body can feel that way. It's *great* – I recommend it!'

Many of our correspondents however described their orgasms without mentioning any anatomical parts. For them the first words that sprang to mind were more concerned with mental pictures and sensations in the head rather than feelings in the body.

'Like going to the top of a mountain, along the plateau then coming down the other side,' said one 48-year-old.

While another forty-something in a happy second marriage said: 'It can be like floating on top of a wave – surfing almost . . . out of control. My mind sees pictures and I'm in another world. It's almost an out of the body experience.'

Several women alluded to waves and foam. 'It's like riding a wave and then crashing down the other side,' said Sue. 'Sorry if this sounds as if I've been watching too many adverts, but it's true!'

A 57-year-old with a great sexual appetite told us that: 'The experience of orgasm never fails to amaze – no matter how many of them you have.'

And a thirty-year-old woman in a very satisfying and happy relationship just said: 'D.H. Lawrence describes my orgasms as I feel them.'

But Kerry from Ireland described her orgasms in great visual detail: 'Imagine a coil of wire with a match on top,' she wrote, 'then touch the bottom of the coil. The vibrations slowly travel through, increasing in intensity until, if you're lucky, the match ignites. The afterglow is the warm match slowly cooling down.'

And, finally, Maria, a woman who described herself to us as someone who'd never been pretty, or rich, and who had had many troubles in her life.

'Orgasm,' she says, 'is a gift from the gods. Sometimes you simply cannot believe how wonderful it feels – it's truly amazing. And – best of all, *it's free!*'

6

THE VARIOUS TYPES OF ORGASM IN WOMEN

Yes, There are Various Types! • Vaginal Orgasms • Clitoral Orgasms • G-spot Orgasms • Nipple Orgasms • Orgasms Through Fantasy Alone • Spontaneous Orgasms • Dream Orgasms • Therapeutic Orgasms • Trans-sexual Orgasm

YES, THERE ARE VARIOUS TYPES!

It's easy to assume that all female orgasms are caused in the same way – but they aren't. Females can be induced to climax in a variety of ways, not all of which involve stimulating the genitals. Possible types of orgasm include:

- vaginal orgasms;
- clitoral orgasms;
- G-spot orgasms;
- nipple orgasms;
- orgasms caused by fantasy;
- spontaneous orgasms;
- dream orgasms.

In this chapter, we'll discuss all of these. We'll also tell you about *therapeutic* orgasms – and about the type of climaxes experienced by trans-sexual women.

VAGINAL ORGASMS

Thanks to Freud, the father of psycho-analysis, people used to believe that vaginal orgasms were what *mature* women had, while clitoral orgasms were 'immature'.

Amazingly this theory persisted until the 1960s and doubtless made untold numbers of women very miserable indeed. One of us (C.W.) remembers in the early 1960s reading a sex education book that advised girls not to masturbate too much in case they got fixated on the clitoris and couldn't make the progression to 'grown-up' sex with a husband when the time came.

Thankfully life has changed! Clitoral orgasms are now considered OK. But our survey has shown that some women have their orgasms during intercourse with no clitoral stimulation and that many of these ladies feel that what happens in the vagina produces their orgasms. They may have orgasms through the presence of their partner's penis, or through vigorous finger play in the vagina itself. But they're convinced that the vagina sparks off orgasm and they talk of the great pleasure they derive from the spasms and contractions they feel deep inside them.

Indeed, some of this group say that clitoral stimulation does nothing for them at all.

Many sex experts would dispute the view that vaginal orgasm exists. They say that vaginal stimulation 'only works because it pulls on the clitoris'. This may or may not be so.

CLITORAL ORGASMS

In the late 1960s and through the 1970s Freud's theories about orgasm were widely rejected and the clitoris became the *vital* organ. In particular, the women's movement lauded this little part of the female anatomy, and women everywhere generally felt much better about themselves, and their needs.

In our survey the vast majority of females told us that the clitoris was essential in their orgasms.

A 36-year-old claimed: 'My husband could push himself, or anything else, in and out of my vagina all night and nothing would happen. I *have* to have my clitoris rubbed. That's what produces orgasms for me and that's all there is to it.'

And other women explained how the clitoris is the core of their sexual-response system: 'It's the key to all sexual feelings,' said a twenty-year-old. 'That's where my orgasm happens. There's no doubt about it.'

Other women who acknowledge that they like and need clitoral stimulation are less clear about what produces that all-important climax.

As a 42-year-old put it:

'I can't climax without my clitoris being very involved.
But I don't find it that easy to climax with *just* clitoral
stimulation. I feel a great need to have something in my
vagina, too, so that when I come I can feel my orgasmic
contractions closing round whatever is in there. I *think*
my orgasm is caused by my clitoris, but I feel the
sensations throughout my whole genital area and
especially in my vagina. So I'm not totally sure about it.
But I suppose as long as I keep having these great
feelings, I'm not that bothered.'

G-SPOT ORGASMS

In Chapter One we explained about the G-spot and where it's
supposed to be. It seems possible that some women can
come as a result of having this area rubbed. We didn't ask
people specifically about the G-spot in our survey, which may
be the reason why so very few of our correspondents
mentioned it.

About fifteen years ago, however, it was all the rage and
you were nobody if you didn't have your orgasms that way –
unless you were a man, of course. It should be said that those
women who *did* write to us about the G-spot were very
enthusiastic about the feelings it produced.

A forty-year-old told us how she'd been amazed when the
G-spot became such big news in 1983. Up till then, she had
assumed that the particularly strong sensations she had felt
whenever a lover's penis or finger pressed halfway up the
front wall of her vagina were unique to her:

'It was a big surprise to discover that my "special bit"
had a name. Before that I believe I'd just always known
that there was this small area inside which could

elevate me into a different orbit if it got some attention.

'Not all men are good at finding it – and my fingers aren't long enough to get there myself – but it's marvellous when it happens and guarantees a big climax.

'My belief is that on those occasions my orgasm actually stems from the G-spot and it makes me squirt some liquid, which doesn't happen with a normal (clitoral) orgasm.'

The question of liquid arose with two other women who claimed that they definitely ejaculated lots of fluid – not urine – when they had G-spot orgasms.

But a 48-year-old secretary wrote to say that though she loved to have her G-spot stimulated, she still had to have her clitoris rubbed at the same time in order to come.

'I'm not sure what causes those orgasms,' she said. 'They're very intense, but I've heard that other women sort of ejaculate when their G-spots are involved, and I don't.'

So, the jury is still out on G-spot orgasms. But some of our female respondents definitely believe they occur.

NIPPLE ORGASMS

Can women have orgasms just as a result of nipple stimulation – without anyone touching their clitorises? Yes, this can happen – but only to a minority of females. In a study of a special group of 'highly orgasmic females' for their book *Ultimate Pleasure* (St Martin's Press, New York), Marc and Judith Meshorer found that no less than 20 per cent of this impressive body of ladies could climax through having their nipples stroked or sucked. One of their subjects claimed to have 'a wire from my breasts straight into my vagina'.

But among women in general, the ability to come by means of nipple stimulation alone is rare. We have found very few people who can do this. However, as mentioned on page 57, some women do accidentally climax while breastfeeding – which shows you what an intensely sensitive place the nipple is.

The occasional woman who can orgasm through having her nipple or areola (the disc *round* the nipple) rubbed is usually very proud of the ability. Hilary, who runs a well-known women's health charity, told us: 'I'm not terribly orgasmic in other ways. But if you touched my tits in Times Square, I'd come there and then!'

If you're a man, *please* don't start expecting your partner to climax through nipple stimulation alone – because it's quite unlikely that she'll be able to do so. But the nipples *are* enormously erotic places, so licking, kissing, sucking and stroking them will nearly always help your lady along the road to orgasm.

ORGASMS THROUGH FANTASY ALONE

Can women achieve orgasm just through fantasising about sex?

We know it sounds a bit fantastic, but it is actually true. In 1992, a paper in the medical journal *Archives of Sexual Behavior*, by Whipple, Ogden and Komisaruk reported a careful study of ten New Jersey ladies who had claimed to be able to climax just through thinking erotic thoughts.

These were not particularly young women: the average age was almost forty-five; two had passed the menopause, and one had had a hysterectomy.

All of them agreed to be tested in the laboratory of the College of Nursing at Rutgers University, where they were hooked up to various scientific monitoring devices. Eight out of the ten were able to produce an orgasm there and then, using sexual 'imagery' alone – the orgasms being confirmed by the medical monitoring equipment.

Interestingly, the authors of the paper say that some of the women showed 'vigorous muscular movement' while they were thinking erotic thoughts, but others lay completely still. This does seem to suggest that it's possible for a climax to originate *in the mind alone*, without any genital stimulation at all.

One further finding of this piece of research was that the women's 'pain thresholds' increased significantly while they were sexually excited. The fact that sex and orgasm make pain more bearable is discussed under the heading 'Therapeutic Orgasms' below.

SPONTANEOUS ORGASMS

Men can sometimes have spontaneous orgasms – usually in times of great stress, as we'll see in Chapter Eleven. But can it happen to women? Can a female just be 'struck' out of the blue by a climax for no apparent reason?

It appears so – but it's a very rare occurrence. One of our survey respondents is Emma, who describes herself as 'a bubbly but level-headed 28-year-old legal assistant'. She says that on a couple of occasions she has been greatly worried about some problem – and then has suddenly found her body being shaken by a powerful orgasm 'which arrived out of nowhere'.

However, she does add: 'In all honesty, I must tell you that I was wearing tight jeans on each occasion, so I suppose it's possible that they could have been rubbing against my clitoris.'

Rather similarly, Hester (who is in the film business) tells us:

'I was flying from my home in Canada to see a dear friend in the Mid-West of the USA. He was quite sick, and I was worried about him.

'I was due to change planes at Minneapolis/St Paul, and we were late getting there. I was terribly worried that I was going to miss the connecting flight.

'To get to the departure gate, I had to sit on some kind of big baggage-buggy, which took forever to rumble through this long, long airport. Halfway to the Gate, I suddenly found myself coming. I guess it was the anxiety. By the way – I got the flight.'

Anxiety also features in another case. Ghislaine, a TV presenter, was rushing desperately in her little car to get to a live programme in Paris. She says: 'I was going wild, because I knew I had to be on screen in thirty minutes and I was still fifteen kilometres away. The *périphérique* was blocked up with traffic, and I was in such a state that I couldn't even change gear.

'Then to my astonishment, I climaxed. I felt a lot calmer after that.'

DREAM ORGASMS

Sexy dreams are supposed to be the province of the male. But, as we saw in Chapter Three, several women told us that they had their very first orgasms that way. In addition a few of our respondents told us that orgasms through dreams are part of their sexual repertoire – albeit an occasional one.

A highly orgasmic forty-something, who is currently without a partner, said that her climaxes in dreams happen without any genital stimulation, as far as she can tell. She also said that they're incredibly intense and she's jolly pleased to have them!

THERAPEUTIC ORGASMS

So many women told us of the 'healing' effect of their
orgasms that we felt we must include some examples in this
chapter. For years we've believed that orgasms can ease
period pain. And many women have written in to our various
newspaper and magazine columns confirming our view that
a climax can alleviate menstrual cramps and spasms.

We also remember one magazine journalist confiding in us
that when she had a painful period she used to masturbate to
orgasm in her car before work, or in the cloakroom during
the day. 'It's the only way I can keep going,' she said.

But several women who took part in our survey believe
that orgasms can help other conditions.

Several people maintained that orgasms cure headaches.
Another woman who suffers from urinary problems believes
that 'a gentle orgasm can relieve the pain of cystitis on
occasions'.

Then there was a thirty-year-old in a very sexually
fulfilling relationship. Some time ago she underwent
emergency surgery to remove an ovarian cyst. She said:

> 'It took about two months before I could consider
> intercourse again but my partner stimulated me orally
> from the day after I returned from hospital.
>
> 'I was scared to allow myself to climax at first as I was
> in considerable pain, but when I did, it was wonderfully
> soothing and relaxing. I fancy it sped up my recovery
> no end!'

Finally one of the women we surveyed was convinced that
strong orgasms had induced labour on two occasions when
her babies were reluctant to put in an appearance.

'Each time these orgasms were really powerful, so at least
I started labour with a smile on my face!'

Incidentally, medical researchers in America have now

proved that orgasms do raise a woman's pain threshold significantly. They've found that immediately after having an orgasm a woman is much more resistant to painful stimuli than she was beforehand – in other words, the mere fact of having climaxed reduces her awareness of pain.

TRANS-SEXUAL ORGASM

There's hardly a person alive who hasn't wondered at some time what their partner actually *feels* at orgasm. The truth is that no woman can know for sure what a man's orgasmic sensations are like. And no man can understand what orgasm is like for a female.

So, we decided to ask someone who has actually been both a man *and* a woman to describe the differences as she sees it.

Janice was born male – biologically. She told us that from her earliest times she felt she was trapped in the wrong body. But as far as her physical equipment was concerned, she grew up as a perfectly normal boy.

As a male, she went to university and later married. She would be the first to admit that she was unhappy as a man and that therefore her experience of male orgasm may not have been typical.

This is how she described a male climax to us: 'Orgasm as a man was an outburst . . . a physical release. I was pleased to have it, but it was no big deal.'

After years of trauma and treatment, Janice emerged as a woman. Now she is a lesbian with an active and happy sex life. She says that orgasms today are entirely central to her being:

'They're totally different from the male ones and involve a lot more feeling. They're very emotional . . . marvellous deep sensations, and I always have five or six during a session. I'm forty now and I suppose if I were a man I wouldn't be having five orgasms every time I made love, would I? I'd probably be lucky to have that many in a week. And there's no way they'd be so good!'

7

WHAT STOPS WOMEN GETTING THERE?

All Sorts of Things Stop Us • Husbands From Hell • The 'Roll-On, Roll-Off' Romeo • The 'Look, No Hands' Lover • The Hubby in a Hurry • The Chap Who Comes too Quickly • The Awful Things Men Say • Sexual Hang-Ups • The Habit of Faking • Alcohol and Drugs • Fatigue • The 'I Don't Orgasm' Syndrome

ALL SORTS OF THINGS STOP US

Most women don't feel utter failures in life if they can't drive a car, but they're often consumed with shame if they can't have an orgasm, or if they find climaxing difficult. Yet, as we've already seen in this book, learning to come can be much harder than passing the driving test!

All manner of things prevent that magical Big O from happening. Many problems are in women's own minds, or in their own habits, but we'll start by looking at the partners who give us a whole lot of trouble.

HUSBANDS FROM HELL

We hope you haven't got one of these, because they're no fun at all. A Husband From Hell comes in from work, switches on the TV, opens the first of many cans of lager, or a bottle of wine, and slumps into his favourite chair. After this flurry of activity he'll be unlikely to move again for hours. He'll eat supper off a tray to avoid missing any television programmes and he'll hardly notice his wife, let alone ask about her day, or compliment her on her appearance.

But then, just before bedtime, his thoughts will turn to his marital rights, so he'll make a clumsy attempt to stroke his partner's thigh. Then, in bed, he'll pat her bottom and insist on giving her a boozy kiss on the lips. (Husbands from Hell *never* kiss their wives on the lips, unless they want sex.)

The Husband From Hell will often become very petty, or even violent, if his wife refuses sex. So, usually, she lets him have intercourse, even though it gives her no pleasure at all and she's forgotten what an orgasm is, if she ever knew.

Husbands From Hell don't seem to know, or care, that women *can't* turn on a sexual tap of desire and that they need nurturing and appreciation. Sadly, vast numbers of their partners *never* have orgasms.

But can anything be done? Well, not one single woman in our survey who described a Husband From Hell had stayed married to him. In fact it may be that women can't admit they have such a terrible relationship until they've left it.

However, we'd like to believe that it's possible for such unpromising men to reform. So if you're unfortunate enough to be in a relationship with a real rotter like this, we would urge you to turn off the television and read Chapter Ten of this book to him – loudly. He MAY just get the message.

THE 'ROLL-ON, ROLL-OFF' ROMEO

We call these men 'Ro-Ro' lovers because they're exactly like those vehicle ferries where the cars have no sooner rolled on than they're rolling off again! Nearly every woman will have met this type, even if she's been wise enough not to settle with it.

The strange thing about Ro-Ro men is that they can be charming, and the life and soul of the party. They can be intelligent, too, but their education is lacking in one *vital* department – they haven't a clue what 'love-play' is. For these guys a clitoris might as well be a climbing plant and the G-spot something to do with furniture.

This means that when they have sex they roll on to their partner, have her (often with indecent haste), and then roll off again and fall asleep (see Figure 7.1).

Some of them *may* be shy. Women's sexual organs are something of a mystery to *women* after all, so it's hardly surprising that men are frequently unsure of the layout between women's legs – *but this is no excuse for not finding out.*

Cara, a very attractive television actress, told us how after

Fig. 7.1

several months of Ro-Ro love-making she dared to broach the subject of clitoral stimulation. Her lover carried on humping as he muttered the memorable words, 'Oh, that's never done much for me, dear!'

Another women with a Ro-Ro husband, weary of yet another bout of totally unsatisfactory sex, grabbed her man's hand and plonked it right on her throbbing clitoris.

Ro-Ro sprang back as if he'd been burnt. Then he recovered himself and remarked that his ex-wife would have been *most* surprised if he'd started touching her *there*. She hadn't needed all that, you see.

Cunning bastard! This is a favourite Ro-Ro trick. He gets away with his selfish behaviour by implying that other women have orgasms without any finger stimulation – thus making his partner feel inadequate. We know this, because wives of Ro-Ros write to us all the time fearing that they're frigid.

A Ro-Ro rarely mends his ways, as Lisa, the ex-wife of one of them discovered.

She'd finally seen the light, dumped Ro-Ro and found herself a man who loved making *her* come. To her surprise old Ro-Ro found himself a new woman quite quickly. Lisa said:

> 'He was gloating as he told me about her. He said he'd been to bed with her and that it had been marvellous. All my old insecurities rose to the surface. Perhaps I really was hopeless in bed if another woman could go to bed with my ex and have orgasms with him. But then he went into more detail.
>
> ' "The only thing was," he said, "when I'd finished, she turned over and masturbated. It was a bit embarrassing. I've never seen anyone do that before." '

Lisa told us that she hadn't known whether to laugh or cry at this revelation. She then wondered if she should tell him a few home truths.

'But I couldn't find the words,' she said. 'I was just too worn out by him and his arrogance and all that awful roll-on, roll-off sex.'

THE 'LOOK, NO HANDS' LOVER

This chap is infinitely preferable to the Husband from Hell and the Ro-Ro. But although he can be persuaded to stimulate the clitoris and offer some foreplay, deep down he believes that 'No Hands' intercourse is the method of sex that nature intended.

He'll rub his woman's clitoris rather perfunctorily, but he still cherishes a dream where penetration and manful thrusting is all it takes for his partner to experience the most earth-shattering climax of her life.

The trouble with these men is that they've seen too many films where this is exactly what happens. Joanna, a bright thirty-year-old woman described her husband to us thus: 'He wants me to have orgasms, and loves it when I do, but recently he asked, "Couldn't we climax together without all that twiddling – just the natural way, in the missionary position – just once?"'

Joanna told us that this is something she's never managed as yet, though she knows some women can do it. She needs lots of continuous rubbing of her clitoris and if she doesn't get it, she doesn't experience the Big O. In fact she reckons the only way she could have an orgasm during intercourse in the missionary position is if she did it with an octopus – and even then he might have to be double-jointed!

Hazel, a librarian in her late thirties told us that her 'Look, No Hands' husband is very lazy about foreplay:

'He seems to think that if he humps away at me for long enough all will be well. I haven't the heart to tell him that unless my mind has been sexually engaged and then I've had lots of kissing and stroking, he could drive a three ton truck up my vagina and it wouldn't have any effect.

'I do get warm and pleasurable contracting feelings deep inside sometimes, but I can't summon them up unless I've had a lot of loving beforehand. I wish penetration on its own gave me orgasms. It would be so much more convenient. But it doesn't. And that's that.'

Sadly this kind of ill-informed lover still exists in a much younger generation – though we have good reason to believe that many young men are more considerate than their fathers were. We also think that some young women simply won't tolerate sexual bad manners like their mums did.

But by no means all female youngsters have the confidence to ask for what they want in bed. A nineteen-year-old wrote on her survey form:

'My boyfriend doesn't seem to realise how much stroking and rubbing I need to get me to orgasm. Or maybe he just can't be bothered to do it for very long. I feel very unsure whether to ask him to go on longer in case he refuses. I feel really pissed off because he gets his pleasure every single time, whereas I don't.'

One final word on the 'Look, No Hands' merchant. We met a guy during our researches who undoubtedly fitted the description of this kind of man. In all seriousness he told us that he thought that women who didn't orgasm with him were just being difficult and rather selfish . . . Oh brother!

THE HUBBY IN A HURRY

This type of man generally has a rough idea about what makes women tick – indeed he prides himself on a knowledge of sexual techniques. And he's good mannered enough to believe that he ought to 'fetch off' his partner before he comes himself. But – he's impatient.

He's almost certainly a Type A personality who arranges his schedule meticulously – so much time for work, so much for golf, so much for sex and so on. His real trouble is that he never quite switches off from his business – he's the guy with the mobile phone on the tennis court!

And though he wants sex, and often quite a lot of it, he wants it at a gallop. It isn't just the wives of these Hubbies in a Hurry who suffer. Men like this often have mistresses – and these poor ladies get the same treatment.

An author friend of ours was having an affair with someone else's Hubby in a Hurry. She told us how she was in bed with him and nearing the point of no return when he suddenly picked up the phone by his bed, dialled his secretary and shouted: 'Ring me if United Biscuits move a point!'

Needless to say our friend didn't ring the bell *that* day.

The Hubby in a Hurry hates to leave you frustrated. It's just that he'd like you to come very quickly – because he's a very busy fellow.

You'll know if your man falls into this category, because when he's short of time he'll rub your clitoris so vigorously that it'll go numb in self-defence, and you'll find yourself wondering why he hasn't developed Repetitive Strain Injury.

Then, as he realises that you're not romping along to a rollicking climax he's likely to raise himself up on to one elbow and ask: 'Are you nearly there, yet?'

Some women tell me they've even had a bloke bellow: 'Haven't you come yet?'

So, guys, *please* remember that women hate being hurried in bed. They *all* say that if a man shows his impatience, they switch off immediately.

THE CHAP WHO COMES TOO QUICKLY

Elsewhere in this book we talk about premature ejaculation and how it can be treated. Women who have trouble in getting all the way to orgasm are *often* involved with men who come too quickly. And, unfortunately, they tend to think that *they* have a problem, when the problem is not theirs at all, but their partner's.

Many women in our survey said that they'd given up expecting an orgasm because their husbands always came too fast. A 38-year-old who told us she felt old before her time said: 'I know my husband's going to climax almost as soon as he gets inside me, so my brain just doesn't engage in sex any more. When your responses are constantly frustrated, it's easier to shut them off completely, rather than put up with any more disappointment.'

Another woman said that she'd forgotten what orgasms

were like because her man kept ejaculating far too soon. She explained that the only reason she continued to have sex with her partner was that *he* enjoyed it – albeit briefly!

'We get on well and do not wish to part,' she said. 'It's a shame, because we used to be much closer. But I have totally switched off and don't know how to switch on again.'

Of course there's absolutely no reason why a guy who comes too soon shouldn't satisfy his partner in other ways, but many women have told us that their husbands are so demoralised by their inability to sustain intercourse that they avoid sexual contact as much as possible.

The answer is clear. If your man persists in climaxing far too soon, then he *must* get treatment – for the sake of your relationship and your sanity. Get him to read Chapter Fourteen of this book too.

THE AWFUL THINGS MEN SAY

There's nothing like an ill-advised remark for knocking a woman off the orgasm trail. One woman told us that a partner instructed her not to talk during love-making. She said this made her very nervous and also led her to believe that he was fantasising about someone else. Needless to say she didn't have orgasms with *him*.

Another woman told us how a new lover found her enthusiastic snogging too much to cope with. 'He asked me to stop opening my mouth so wide. I found this really off-putting. It made me feel as if I wasn't doing anything right. In retrospect I realise that this chap had bags of sexual hang-ups. But I hadn't worked that out at the time and I just thought I was hopeless.'

A 23-year-old said that though it's nice to be encouraged in bed, when that encouragement starts sounding like an order, it's terribly off-putting. She said: 'One guy used to say,

"Come for me, come for me." I hated it – I'm not a fast food restaurant!'

Another young woman of twenty-eight said that she was totally turned off while being penetrated by a new lover for the first time. Apparently he shouted: 'Good God! It's like waving a sausage about in the Albert Hall.'

And a forty-year-old, now in a happy and fulfilling sexual relationship, told us that she'd been reduced to tears by a previous lover. As she was nearing a climax he whispered: 'Hurry up – I've got to meet my girlfriend in an hour.'

Other women reported very unhappy experiences in the bedroom when their men hinted, or even told them outright, that they were overweight.

A forty-year-old told us how her first husband used to sigh audibly when she wanted intercourse with her on top. 'Oh God, you're not going to climb on top of me, are you?' he would say. 'I'll be flattened.'

Try having an orgasm after that!

Another woman felt so resentful about her husband's unkind comments about her weight that she stopped having orgasms with him at all.

'Women very rarely insult men when *they're* overweight,' she said. 'It's hateful for a man to criticise a woman, especially when they're making love. All too often the woman *knows* she's overweight and is battling with her self-esteem anyway. Orgasms don't come easily at the best of times, but I don't even try and have one now.'

Sylvia told us how her ex-lover turned her right off:

'We'd made love the day before and I'd had a really great orgasm for the first time with this particular man.

The next day he came round and we got into bed. But just as I was getting going he said: "You're not going to do all that screaming and writhing about are you? It put me right off my stroke yesterday."'

And Michele told us of the terrible drawbacks of trying to have orgasms with the boss:

'I'd fallen for my married boss – stupid, I know, but one's heart doesn't always choose sensible people. It was a nightmare. He ordered me about in bed like he did in the office. "Open your legs a bit more," he would say. Or "Now, turn over." But the ultimate put-down came when we were staying in this swanky hotel in London. I was really steamed up and approaching orgasm when the phone rang.

'He went rigid, then he snapped at me, "Don't you dare make a sound when I pick up the receiver!"

'"Will it be your wife?" I whispered. "No," he said clasping a hand over my mouth, "it's almost certainly my mistress."'

SEXUAL HANG-UPS

Very strict mothers have a lot to answer for when it comes to their daughters' ability to have orgasms. Some women told us how they'd had to battle for years to rid themselves of their mothers' beliefs.

'She told me that sex was dirty,' said a 27-year-old, 'and I'm only just learning what a marvellous, beautiful thing it is. I had my first orgasm a few months ago – no thanks to my mother.'

Many, many women had been told never to touch themselves 'down below'.

'As an adult you can look back at what your mum said and laugh,' said Sadie, 'but it still takes a lot of courage to throw off her teaching and develop some values of your own.'

But most of our respondents who complained of this kind of negative influence were happy to tell us that they'd gradually overcome their early, restrictive training. However, if a woman cannot fight feelings of revulsion about her body, or if she literally tightens her vaginal muscles into a spasm which prevents intercourse, then she should seek professional help. Problems like these leave a woman very unhappy with herself and will make achieving orgasm very difficult, if not impossible.

Several women in our survey said that their problems with orgasm were due to having been raped when they were younger. One woman told us that she'd never mentioned the incident to anyone before telling us.

Other women had been sexually abused and as a result had never had a satisfactory love life or orgasms in adult life.

We feel that women who've suffered such terrible traumas are unlikely to be able to overcome their problems alone. In the case of rape or child sexual abuse a woman should start by contacting her local Rape Crisis Centre. People there will listen to her and support her. They'll also point her in the direction of more extensive therapy, if that's what's needed.

THE HABIT OF FAKING

There's hardly a woman alive who hasn't faked orgasm at some time in her life. In fact, 60.5 per cent of the respondents to our survey had faked. Even easily orgasmic women sometimes resort to subterfuge in order to save their husbands' feelings, or to get some much needed sleep.

But women who persistently fake are making a rod for their own backs. 'After eleven years of marriage,' said one 34-year-old, 'how can I now turn round and say I want an orgasm? He thinks I have them effortlessly several times a week.'

And a 48-year-old who we surveyed told us that when she decided to tell her long-term lover that he'd never rung the bell for her, he just laughed.

'He couldn't believe what I was saying – in fact, he *refused* to believe it. He said: "Don't give me that rubbish – don't you think I would have known?"'

Many women who regularly faked in the early stages of a marriage or other relationship ended up never, ever having orgasms during the time they were with that partner. Some of them told us that it was far too difficult and embarrassing to own up to faking after years of doing it, so they either carried on doing it, or they left the relationship.

But as one, now extremely orgasmic, 35-year-old said: 'When I met my next partner, I vowed I'd *never* fake it, ever again. I'd faked for twenty years and I knew how damaging it could be. I thank my lucky stars now that I have plenty of orgasms and don't ever pretend.'

ALCOHOL AND DRUGS

Alcohol can be extremely useful in relaxing people and helping them lose their sexual inhibitions – but only in small quantities. A couple of glasses of wine should more than do the trick.

Several of the women we researched told us that they'd had problems with heavy drinking and that this habit completely killed their ability to have orgasms. So please: only use it in moderation.

A word, too, about tranquillisers. Few experts would dispute that there are occasions when a short course of tranquillisers help people over a period of extreme stress, but doctors now agree that long-term use of such drugs should be avoided because people can become addicted to them all too easily.

One side-effect of tranquillisers, particularly when they're taken for too long, is that they deaden desire and can stop women having orgasms. This doesn't seem to be widely known.

Please bear in mind that *any* sedative drug might do the same. If a drug makes you drowsy, it's possible it may interfere with your orgasms.

FATIGUE

We've seen elsewhere in the book how fatigue is a major enemy of the orgasm. Nowadays far too many women are 'juggling' jobs and children and husbands and elderly relatives; in other words, they're trying to be all things to all people. The trouble is that their inevitable exhaustion frequently knocks the possibility of orgasm on the head.

It's easy to see the problem in other people, but folk often miss the signs in themselves. One woman wrote to us to say that she hadn't had an orgasm for two years. But as she went on it became clear why.

She has a full-time job . . . *and* a part-time one. She looks after her ageing mother on Sundays, she has a husband and two teenage daughters at home and also a schizophrenic son whose behaviour is so unpredictable that she has to arrange constant supervision for him. Needless to say, she worries about all the elements in her life, all the time. She also sleeps badly and she and her husband don't have any time together except when they crash into bed too worn out for anything but a very occasional 'quickie'.

It's easy to say that this woman must cut out some of her work, find time for herself and learn to pamper her body – but it won't be easy for her to rearrange her life.

One thing is abundantly clear: women are not machines, and female orgasms frequently depend upon women's bodies and minds being in reasonable shape.

We can't tell women what to do with their lives, but in general terms if they want to have great orgasms and fruitful relationships then they have to eliminate some tasks from their crowded schedules, and some stress from their over-worked minds.

THE 'I DON'T ORGASM' SYNDROME

Some women who find climaxing difficult have told us that they admit their difficulties right at the start of a new relationship. This *can* be a very good idea. It frequently makes a woman feel less pressurised and sometimes, as a result, she becomes less tense and actually experiences the Big O. A sympathetic, gentle, caring man helps, of course.

But there are women who announce rather aggressively to any new guy: 'I DON'T ORGASM'.

This may get the dreaded subject out of the way, but it's doing these women no favours at all. They condition themselves into believing that orgasm is impossible for them and they tend to end up with guys who are only too pleased not to have to bother making the ladies come.

A woman like this *can* change, but she usually needs to meet a thoroughly decent man who loves her, and who is determined to bring her pleasures of which she never dreamt.

She could also read our next chapter . . .

8

<u>HOW TO GET THERE IF YOU NEVER</u>
<u>HAVE</u>

Step One: Realise You're Not Alone
Step Two: Learn about Your Body and You
Step Three: Pleasure Yourself
Step Four: Now You Can Do It – Do It With Him
Step Five: Do It During Intercourse

STEP ONE: REALISE YOU'RE NOT ALONE

The first thing to realise is that you're not alone in your problems with orgasm, so *definitely* don't give up the struggle.

Our researches have shown that many bright, intelligent, pretty women have had enormous difficulty in climaxing for the first time. So if you've never had an orgasm, don't think you're a freak – you're not.

Whatever your age, we want you to read this chapter carefully and follow the plan we've devised to get *you* to orgasm. Before long we hope you'll have this unique, joyous, relaxing and magical experience for yourself. You *can* do it . . .

STEP TWO: LEARN ABOUT YOUR BODY AND YOU

We want you to do some things that will make you feel better about yourself. You see, what we've learned from women who've achieved orgasm after a long and difficult battle is this:

- they've put themselves first;
- they've taken control of the challenge to climax.

Many of these women started with very poor self-esteem, but at one critical point in their lives they decided that they were worthwhile, lovable people who *deserved* to have orgasms. Then they set about learning how to have them.

Good self-esteem often stems from knowing your body better and liking it more. So we want you to start by taking a good look at your naked self in the mirror. Instead of letting your eyes zoom in on all the bits you don't care for, we want you to make a mental list of your good points.

Then we want you to stand and admire them – and stroke them, lovingly. We hope you think your breasts are great, or your bottom, but even if it's just your ankles – then stroke them!

Then we want you to take a decision to improve something about yourself that you *don't* like. If you're out of condition, vow to walk to work instead of taking a bus. If you're overweight, join a slimming club. If your breasts are drooping, go to a gym and learn some exercises that will perk them up again, or take up swimming – which should work wonders.

Now, you may say that you've gone on a diet before, or started to exercise, but that you haven't stuck to it. But this time it's different. You're in training to become orgasmic, so you've a *very* good reason for carrying on. We're only asking you to make *one* improvement after all. And the reason for it is this: *once you believe that you can control your body, even in a small way, having an orgasm will become very much easier.*

Many women have told us that their tension used to get in the way of having orgasms. As we saw in Chapter Four, even easily orgasmic women often fail to achieve a climax when they are tense about their work schedules or all their family commitments.

So the next step in our bid to get you to orgasm is to persuade you to relax properly.

This is another way in which you can take control of your own body. Try lying flat on the bed. Breathe in really deeply as far as you can. Then hold the breath for as long as you're able – it should become a bit uncomfortable towards the end – then breathe out fully.

You could well be amazed at the feeling – many folk are so tense these days that they normally never completely inflate, or deflate their lungs.

Repeat this exercise ten times. Then gradually relax your whole body. Here's how to do it:

- breathe in and out slowly and deeply all the time you're relaxing. Then, tighten your feet, hold the tension, then relax. Breathe in and out slowly and deeply again.
- then tense the muscles in your lower legs – hold – then release. Breathe in and out slowly and deeply.
- continue in this way right up to the neck.
- the neck is often one of the most tense bits of you, so try turning your head to the left *at the same time as* trying to turn your head to the right. This may sound odd, but it builds up the most extraordinary feelings of tension in the neck and shoulders. Hold this for at least five seconds, then relax fully. This should bring immense relief and feel *marvellous* – not as good as the relaxation after an orgasm though!

At this stage you may feel you'd like to learn more about relaxation – and if you want to take it further, then do. It can only help.

Most bookshops, chemists and healthfood shops sell relaxation sound tapes. Or you might decide to give Yoga a try, or even hypnosis, with a properly qualified practitioner.

Finally, in this section about your body, we want you to take a hand mirror into the bedroom, make yourself comfortable and look at your genitals.

Now some sex manuals insist that a woman must learn to love her pink bits, if she's to become orgasmic. But we know many, highly orgasmic women who have never found themselves very attractive 'down below'. So if you don't think you're that sensational in that area, please don't lose heart.

What's vital, however, is for you to look at exactly what you've got between your legs. Your clitoris is the most important part. It's hidden in the genital folds right at the top of the whole arrangement of bits and pieces and it's about the size of a pea. Make friends with this little organ, because it's going to give you enormous pleasure in the years to come.

Lick your fingers and gently feel your clitoris. Your sensations should indicate when you're right on it. Then carefully stroke to one side of it, then the other. Lie back and consider how you're feeling. Is it nice? It should be. But don't rush it. It's time now to take a look at the rest of your genitals.

About an inch down from the clitoris is a tiny hole which is where you pee from. You might not even be able to see this hole in the mirror, but you can feel it with your finger.

You'll know you're on it when you have a slight urge to pass water.

Lower down again you'll see a much larger hole. This is the vagina. This is where you bleed from when you have a period. And it's where babies emerge from. If you've already had a child, or two, you'll know all about this bit of you!

Now, whether or not you feel you have lovely genitals, we want you to accept that most men *adore* women's private parts. More importantly we want you to realise that your genital area is stuffed full of nerve endings which can provide you with the most exquisite feelings known to man or woman.

They're yours to enjoy – and you will.

STEP THREE: PLEASURE YOURSELF

In an ideal world you should take several weeks over the previous section before starting on this part of our programme.

We know you're anxious to get on with it! But don't neglect those important steps to self-approval, self-improvement and self-relaxation. In fact, as you progress now to more direct touching, we want you to start every session by standing before a mirror and saying:

'I am lovely. I am sexy. I deserve to have good feelings
– and lots of orgasms.'

It doesn't matter if you laugh while you're saying these
three sentences, or even if you think they're stupid – just say
them. In time your mind will accept these messages and
you'll begin to believe them.

We'd like you to think of the next three months of your life
as *your* time.

This is when you're going to learn to have an orgasm. It
might happen sooner than you think, or it might even take
longer than a few months, but it's important that you reserve
this time for you.

Imagine if you were going to take a degree – you'd have to
allocate three *years* to it, but you wouldn't feel guilty. Well
now you're embarking on your own personal course to
achieve orgasm, and you need adequate time to do it.

A word of warning: it's no use at all trying to follow our
programme hurriedly while your partner and children are
watching TV downstairs. You'll never relax that way, because
you'll be worrying all the time that someone will come in and
disturb you. So do arrange to be on your own in the house
for a period of two hours, a couple of times a week.

If this is absolutely impossible – for example if your
partner is unemployed and never goes out – then you may
have to tell him that you're taking a special course in
relaxation and that you need a couple of times a week when
you can be entirely private.

If you have a partner with whom you share everything,
then by all means tell him that you're working towards
having an orgasm. But *don't* let him watch at this stage, or
interrupt you. Your *pleasure time* should be sacred and you
should feel secure in the knowledge that it's a window in
your routine twice a week, for you alone.

Begin each two-hour session by having an unhurried hot,
scented bath. Make sure that your bathroom is warm, and as

romantic looking as possible. You might like to take your bath by candlelight – this can help to evoke a special atmosphere.

Think kindly thoughts about yourself in the bath and also encourage sexy fantasies. Imagine you're being teased all over by Mel Gibson – if he's your heart-throb – or Hugh Grant.

Or if you're from an earlier generation, conjure up the image of Robert Redford, or even someone no longer with us like Cary Grant or Charles Boyer. This is *your* fantasy and by the power of your own thought you can make dead men young again, and enslaved by you.

If you have a partner whom you dearly love, cast your mind back to the first time he kissed you, or recall the heady excitement as his fingers brushed against your breast for the first time. If you have a showerhead attachment in your bathtub, you might care to use it to caress your breasts and then your private parts. Many women report that this makes them feel very sexy and some have even learned to climax this way.

When you're ready, dry yourself carefully and lovingly and move into your bedroom which should be warm, and looking as romantic and beautiful as possible.

You're going to start by lying on the bed and anointing your whole body with body lotion. Don't feel threatened; all you have to do is to rub this nice emollient into your arms and your feet and your tummy and your breasts and your thighs.

Take your time, and enjoy the sensations as the lotion caresses your body.

If you like music, play a favourite disc in the background. Relax – enjoy yourself. It's long overdue.

When you're ready to move on to feeling your genitals, we suggest you switch to a lubricant especially designed for the purpose, like Senselle or K-Y Jelly, just in case your body lotion causes any irritation of your most delicate tissues. We strongly advise the use of lubricants while you're touching yourself up. They help your fingers to glide over your most intimate bits, and will increase your excitement.

In your own time, start gently to explore between your legs. Put two fingers into your vagina and move them around. Then relax and think about the feelings you're having.

Next, take a moistened finger and gently stroke the area around your clitoris. Try stroking below it, then above, next to one side, then the other. Discover what you like best and then do it some more.

You might begin to feel that you're establishing a kind of rhythm to your caresses, and that they're taking you somewhere.

Relax and breathe deeply. This is your *pleasure time*. Enjoy it.

Take this stroking and caressing as far as you want – and no further.

Perhaps your feelings won't be very strong initially. Or maybe they'll seem quite powerful. They may even frighten you a little and you might decide you've done enough for one day. This is your choice, but now you've started the programme, it'll become easier to do it and you'll get keener on returning to it.

In other sessions you might want to experiment a little more.

Some women find that stroking round the clitoris, or indeed right on it, feels even nicer when they put a finger or two from their left hand into the vagina.

Many women find that reading erotic literature while rubbing the clitoris builds great excitement in their minds, which translates into heightened sensations in the body.

And countless women have told us that a vibrator got them to their first climax when everything else had failed and they'd almost given up hope. So if you want to use a vibrator in these sessions, go ahead. But always start with your body massage first, and then a little lubricated finger-stroking. Your own hands are much warmer and softer than a vibrator – and more sensuous, too.

As the weeks progress, you should find that you're more in control of your body and that you're experiencing better feelings than you've ever been able to have before.

You'll also find that your mind is becoming more adept at getting your sexy sensations going. But don't worry if occasionally nothing seems to go right. Rome wasn't built in a day, and learning a new skill tends to be an erratic process rather than a reliable, steady and logical progression.

If you're in a relationship, you'll probably be having sex with your partner during the period that you're learning to pleasure yourself.

Don't be disheartened if that sex doesn't suddenly improve. Your present aim is to have an orgasm by yourself, and *for* yourself. Of course you might find that all the extra stimulation you're getting suddenly catapults you into the ecstasy of orgasm with your partner, but it's not very likely.

By all means start introducing the new strokes and caresses you've been learning into your sex sessions, but don't be disappointed if they don't yet work as well with your partner as they do on your own.

What's most likely to happen is that one day, during your pleasure time, you'll feel specially relaxed and increasingly turned on. Your feelings will direct your fingers to become more insistent. You'll start rubbing directly on your clitoris, where previously you tended to rub round it. Your breathing will quicken and you'll feel warmer and warmer.

You won't be quite sure what's happening, but you'll know that you're desperate for it to continue. Love yourself. Stroke other parts of your body if you've got a free hand, and give in to the feelings that are taking hold of you.

The build-up of feeling and tension will be immense, and then – suddenly – your body will be flooded with the best feeling in the world. It'll take over your mind and your whole being and fill you with indescribable pleasure. Just lie back and absorb the beauty of the moment. This is your first orgasm – and you've waited a long time for it.

STEP FOUR: NOW YOU CAN DO IT – DO IT WITH HIM

If you have a partner, you'll probably want to share your triumph with him as soon as possible. Indeed, many women have told us that once they'd achieved their first orgasm, they quickly went to bed with a partner and immediately came again with him.

But you might decide that you'd like to wait a while and have a few more orgasms on your own before involving your man. If this is how you feel, then follow your instincts. But when the time comes to put your new-found skill into practice, how should you do it?

If you're very comfortable with your partner and you want him to touch and caress you right away, then go ahead. But show him what you want, or tell him. Don't leave it to chance.

Alternatively, sit him some way away from you so he can see everything but not touch, and then touch yourself and bring yourself to orgasm.

If he's not too near you, you'll be able to concentrate on your own technique. But be warned: if your partner is a normal hot-blooded male, he'll probably find the sight of you touching yourself up so arousing that he'll want to leap on you before you've finished.

Be firm. You're putting on a show for him to prove that you can climax with someone else watching, and also to demonstrate to him what works for you.

When you're ready to invite him to touch and caress you and help you to a climax, it would almost certainly be best to do this through hand-petting initially, as this method will most closely mimic what you've been doing to yourself. You might then find you'd like to move on to having oral sex.

Many women find this the easiest way of all to climax, but don't be too impatient too soon. If you get him to perform cunnilingus on you, but you sense that you're not going to be able to reach orgasm that way on that day, then either finish yourself off through masturbation or encourage your partner to do it for you by manual love play.

If you've developed a taste for bringing yourself to orgasm while you have either a vibrator or your fingers inside you, then you might find that you'll come more easily during oral sex if your lover puts his fingers inside you at the same time as he is licking or kissing your clitoris.

It'll take time to increase your orgasmic repertoire, but what fun you'll have doing it!

STEP FIVE: DO IT DURING INTERCOURSE

If you have a partner, there will come a time when you long to be able to have your orgasm with him *during intercourse*. But don't be disappointed if this doesn't happen to order. It could well be the most difficult hurdle of all. Many of the women we surveyed told us that they'd *never* managed to come during actual intercourse. So regard this particular part of your sex menu as a bonus, rather than a necessity.

But one thing is vital. If you feel that you need to have control of your own clitoris at this stage of your orgasmic development, then do so. It's your clitoris and you can rub it yourself if you want to.

Most men will be quite happy about this and lots of them will be really turned on. But if your man doesn't like it, he's going to have to learn to lump it – for now, anyway.

What we suggest, when it comes to attempting orgasm *during* intercourse, is that you try positions where you can control the pace – and also have easy access to your clitoris.

Many intercourse positions involve the man's weight resting on the woman, so that it can be quite a problem for either partner to stroke the clitoris. Also, men love positions where *they* control the pace, and can thrust very deeply. Instead, we recommend that you try one or both of two suggestions of ours: suggestions which will put *you* firmly in charge!

In both of these positions, the woman gets to feel a slightly different and softer-seeming part of the penis than usual. This full softness bulges just inside her vaginal opening, which can give her really wonderful sensations. Here are the two positions:

Free as air

We're indebted here to the researches of top London psychologist Dr Roy Shuttleworth, who says that this position rarely fails to deliver an orgasm in a woman. You can see it in Figure 8.1.

What you do first is to get your partner to lie down flat on his back. Next, you sit down on his erect penis, facing away from him. Incidentally, many men adore this view of a lady.

Then you lean backwards so that you are lying on your man. It may take one or two attempts to get comfortable and to keep his penis inside you, but it's worth persevering. Once you're in place as in Figure 8.1, you'll feel a very pleasant, slightly congested sensation round your vaginal opening. You'll also have a feeling of really being 'free as air' – because you'll have no weight on you at all. And, most important, you can either rub your own clitoris, or get your partner to reach round and do it.

Your man will be unable to thrust very vigorously in this position, so you will definitely control the depth of penetration and, to a large extent, the pace.

If he has very good control, he may be able to stop thrusting and simply hold his penis as deeply inside you as he can *without moving* for a while. This can be an unusual sensation for a woman, and a real turn-on. The feeling of still fullness in your vagina may well drive you wild.

Fig. 8.1

Meanwhile, one or other of you should be rubbing your clitoris like mad. Orgasms should follow . . .

Cuissade position

This one also ensures that the woman can reach her own clitoris easily. Again, she feels in control of how much or how often her partner thrusts into her – and she can use his thigh to stimulate her further.

As shown in Figure 8.2, you lie on your back, while your man lies to the right of you on his left side. He puts his right leg under *your* right one, and across your left thigh. Then his penis will fit in quite easily.

Now you can really concentrate on your own pleasure. Either squeeze his thigh between yours so that it presses up, against your vulva, or else rub your own clitoris. You are in control!

Fig. 8.2

A caring partner will enjoy being 'used' for your pleasure in these two positions. Many men are pleased for a woman to take the initiative once in a while. Also your man should appreciate that your newly acquired knowledge about your body – and about how you can get to orgasm – ought to enrich your relationship.

Finally, if you've gone through this chapter and achieved orgasm, but you *don't* have a partner right now, we hope that you'll continue to have sex 'with yourself' and enjoy it.

Whether or not the right man arrives in your life in the future, you deserve a sex life (and orgasms) just as much as any woman who has a partner. So remember that – and make time for your pleasure.

9

HOW TO HAVE BETTER ORGASMS – A GUIDE FOR WOMEN

Yes, You *Can* Have Better Orgasms – and More of Them
Step One: Get Yourself the Right Man For the Job
Step Two: Get Him to Read Chapter Ten!
Step Three: Make Sure You Make Time For Yourself
Step Four: Always *Tell* Him What You Want In Bed
Step Five: Exercise Your PC Muscle
Step Six: Get Your Man To Use the 'Dual Approach' to Orgasm
Step Seven: Use Fantasy
Step Eight: Don't Hesitate To 'Touch Yourself Up'
Step Nine: Buy a Vibrator
Step Ten: Letting Yourself Have Multiple Orgasms
Step Eleven: Use the Famous CAT – and the PUSSY

YES, YOU *CAN* HAVE BETTER ORGASMS *AND* MORE OF THEM

Yes, you can have better orgasms, and if you want to, you can have more of them! You can be multiply orgasmic if you wish. This chapter will show you how.

However, if you've *never* had a climax (or only hardly ever), this chapter isn't the one for you. Please go back and read Chapters Seven and Eight, which are for women in your situation. Good luck! For everybody else, this chapter presents a guide towards making your orgasms:

* easier;
* more intense and pleasurable;
* more frequent.

Let's go, ladies – let's go!

STEP ONE: GET YOURSELF THE RIGHT MAN FOR THE JOB

If you're messing around in one of those all-too-common relationships where the guy doesn't really want to bother about giving you orgasms, let alone *good* ones, then you are wasting your precious time. Ship out – now!

There is absolutely no point in going to bed with a man who doesn't want to put his heart and soul into making you climax. Get rid of him.

Happily, there are plenty of fellas around who *do* enjoy giving a woman pleasure through gentle, loving sex. Find one, and stick with him.

The only alternative is a lifetime of masturbation . . .

STEP TWO: GET HIM TO READ CHAPTER TEN!

However nice your guy is, and however keen he is on sex and on making you happy, it's unlikely that he's a fully trained sexologist.

So, no matter what he may claim (and men do make prodigious claims for their sexual ability!) it's absolutely inevitable that there's quite a lot he can learn about bedroom manners and bedroom technique. That's not a criticism of him; it's just a fact of life.

Now . . . the things he needs to know in order to give you more and better orgasms are outlined for him in the next chapter – Chapter Ten. Give it to him and – taking care not to put him down in any way – tell him that you'd be really turned on if he would read it, and then try out some of the ideas in it on you.

STEP THREE: MAKE SURE YOU MAKE TIME FOR YOURSELF

One of the curses of modern life is that *women do not allow themselves enough time for sex – and for orgasms.*

This problem is of far more concern to females than it is to males because, of course, the average male can come so much more quickly.

If you want to have quite a few really intense orgasms per week, then you must set aside time in which you and your lover can be together. Ideally, this should be at least *two hours* or so per session. That may seem a lot, but research shows that many women would actually prefer to have an hour or so of love play *before* they move on to intercourse.

Also, the time you allow must be time when you're not

tired out. Exhaustion is the enemy of orgasms!

If your man can't spare as much time as you'd like, then make do with what he *can* spare, but it would be worthwhile considering whether you should allot yourself some additional 'solo' time in which you get yourself into an erotic and relaxed mood. If you organise things well, this could be just before he arrives home, panting for your body (we hope).

STEP FOUR: ALWAYS *TELL* HIM WHAT YOU WANT IN BED

Almost incredibly, our research shows that a lot of women still don't *say* very much in bed. They lie there, taking whatever their lovers 'dish up', and hoping for the best.

This is no good! You're entitled to say what you want, and if you'd like to have good, plentiful climaxes, then you need to tell your man *exactly* what to do.

Do you want oral sex tonight? Then say so. Do you want him to put his finger inside you? Tell him. Do you want him to lick your nipples? He's not telepathic, so put it into words. It's not so difficult!

The next step is to *show* him very precisely what he should be doing. You've asked him to frig your clitoris, and he's doing it for you – but he's a good half-inch away from the spot that would give you maximum pleasure. So move his fingertip to the *right* place, and let him stimulate there instead.

A few men will resent this. Tough.

STEP FIVE: EXERCISE YOUR PC MUSCLE

Your PC muscle (it stands for 'Pubo-Coccygeus') is the one you tighten up when you want to stop yourself passing urine, and also when you want to stop yourself passing a bowel motion.

The *front* part of the muscle stops you peeing, and the *back* part keeps your rectum closed. Unfortunately, this muscle gets in a terrible state in many women – especially those who have had several children. If it gets 'saggy', you may well have problems with your waterworks and possibly your bowels, and you may get a prolapse (descent) of your womb.

So toning up this muscle is good for you, which is why the toning-up exercises are taught to most women while they are pregnant, and just after they've had a baby. However, there's evidence that getting it into good shape will help you enjoy your orgasms more, too.

To have a work-out with the PC muscle:

• tighten up the *front* part (by pretending you're holding back urine). Release. Repeat 20 times.
• tighten up the *back* part (by pretending you're holding back a bowel motion). Release. Repeat 20 times.
• do this morning and evening for at least six months.

As you'll find elsewhere in the book, doing this exercise *during intercourse* will have very nice effects on your man.

STEP SIX: GET YOUR MAN TO USE THE 'DUAL APPROACH' TO ORGASM

Now here's a most important thing for any woman (or man) to know about female climaxes. You stand a much better chance of climaxing – and of having a really *good* one – *if you are receiving two lots of stimulation instead of one.*

By 'two lots of stimulation', we mean both clitoris stimulation *and* vaginal stimulation, both at the same time.

At this point we take off our hats to American *Cosmopolitan* magazine. *Cosmo* was the first to point out – after a large sex survey of its readers – that for two-thirds of women, **combined vaginal and clitoral stimulation is the most effective way of getting an orgasm.**

This extraordinary discovery, made in 1990, has not had the publicity that it deserves! Yet it explains why so many females take a long time to get to a climax – and why they may not enjoy it all that much when they get there.

We cannot over-emphasise how important this *Cosmo* finding could be to you. If you want to have easy, reliable, intense and frequent orgasms, then get your man to make a frequent habit of simultaneously stimulating:

• *your clitoris* – with his finger, lips or tongue – or with a vibrator;
• *your vagina* – so that your S-zone (the first couple of inches or so) is STRETCHED. There are all sorts of ways of stretching the S-zone, with fingers or a with a vibrator – or, indeed, with your man's penis.

So don't forget: for really intense sensation, learn to use the 'dual approach'. If your man can't manage both types of stimulus on his own, there's no reason why you shouldn't help him . . .

STEP SEVEN: USE FANTASY

Fantasising in your head was at one time considered 'improper'. But, as many women have discovered in recent years, it's an extraordinarily good way of :

- speeding your orgasm;
- making it more exciting;
- giving you the chance to have more.

Some females fantasise *without* 'sharing it' with their partners. Research shows that what they most commonly do is to fantasise about having sex with . . . somebody else! Six out of ten women studied have done this. The 'somebody else' is often a famous film or TV star.

If you want to play your fantasies 'solo' like this, then fair enough. In fact, it may sometimes be better to keep quiet about the fact that you're using such imagery – in case your partner might be upset by the idea.

Rather more romantically, a lot of women make a habit of sharing fantasies with their lovers – simply by saying things like 'Let's pretend I'm marooned on a desert island . . . and you're the handsome chief of a native tribe, who decides to deflower me for the Annual Fertility Ceremony . . .'

So go for it: it's astonishing how powerful these harmless fantasies can be in boosting a woman's orgasm.

STEP EIGHT: DON'T HESITATE TO 'TOUCH YOURSELF UP'

If you want to have more and better orgasms, then you need to be prepared to 'touch up' your own clitoris, if necessary. We don't just mean during solo sex. When you're with a male partner – even a very skilled male partner – there will be times when he's too carried away to give that vital need-it-now rub to your clitoral area.

Similarly, there may be occasions when you and he are in some wacky position that leaves his hands at one end of the bed, and your clitoris at the other!

Add to this the fact that many women find that self-stimulation of the clitoris does produce very intense orgasms, and you can see that this is a trick which is well worth having up your sleeve.

You can use it during love play, or you can use it during intercourse – especially when you're making love in a position in which you can easily get fingertips to your clitoris, but he can't.

You can also use it sometimes to stimulate yourself in front of your man. This is very popular with women – especially younger women – as you'll see from our survey.

It's also popular with most men; you can tell this from looking at 'pin-up' magazines, where the young ladies are frequently photographed in attitudes which are intended to suggest that they are busy stimulating themselves.

To give you an example of the sort of sensible use of bedroom masturbation that we're advocating, here's a brief extract from the diary of a highly sexed businesswoman who spent an enjoyable afternoon with her lover:

1 pm	Arrived at hotel with John. Lunch & glass of Chablis.
2.00	Bed. He's in great shape!
2.30	He made me come through cunnilingus. Lovely.
2.35	Brought myself off again while he was resting.
2.45	John gave me another 'O' with his fingers. Mmm . . .
3.05	We both came through intercourse – with a little help from *my* flying fingers!
3.35	He woke up and frigged me again, the naughty boy. With a bit of assistance from me, he made me climax *again*. That's five today.
4.00	Waiter arrived with a nice pot of tea.

As you'll readily appreciate from reading the above rather hectic timetable, a woman who has the ability to 'lend a hand', so to speak, greatly increases her chances of having multiple orgasms (see Step Ten: Letting Yourself Have Multiple Orgasms, on the next page).

STEP NINE: BUY A VIBRATOR

These incredibly inexpensive little devices are now used by huge numbers of women all around the world. And without doubt, they've helped masses of females to have far more climaxes than they would have enjoyed otherwise.

They buzz away reliably, giving a nice, gentle vibration against your clitoris or in your vagina, or wherever you want the added stimulation. Some people like them on their nipples, and some like them between their buttocks – but if you choose that method, *don't* ever put the vibrator inside your bottom; they can get lost up there!

You can use it in three main ways:

* during solo sex;
* during love play – with either you or your man holding it;
* during intercourse – again, with either of you holding it.

During sexual intercourse, a smallish vibrator can even be put *in* the vagina, alongside the man's penis. This is a very useful technique for promoting orgasm in the many instances where the woman's opening has become a little larger owing to childbirth.

From all of this, you can see that a vibrator can be a tremendous aid to having multiple climaxes – see below (if you'll forgive the phrase).

STEP TEN: LETTING YOURSELF HAVE MULTIPLE ORGASMS

If you're happy with having one orgasm at a session, that's fine – don't bother to read this section. But if you do want to be a 'multa', then here are our suggestions:

- first, follow all the advice which we've just given in this chapter. In other words, find the right guy, tell him what you want, allow yourself plenty of time, use fantasy and the 'dual approach' and employ both self-stimulation and a vibrator, whenever you feel like it. In general, use your *easiest* method of getting to orgasm at the beginning of each session.
- next, bear in mind the American research paper which recently showed that multi-orgasmic women tend to be rather more *open-minded* about sex – letting themselves use books, videos or whatever to turn themselves on. They also seem to be very good at compressing their thighs, to put extra pressure on their clitorises!

  So, open your mind to all possibilities, and be ready to accept orgasms from all sorts of sources – including your thighs . . .
- finally, make a note of this vital tip. **The best time to go for the second orgasm of the evening ISN'T an hour or two after the first – it's just a few minutes afterwards.**

Why? Well, as we explained at the start of this book (see page 51), a woman's climax is very different from a man's. In effect, a male 'climbs up a mountain' – and then slides straight down again.

In contrast, a woman achieves the peak – and then slips down just a few metres to have a little rest, only a short distance below the summit. *It's from there that the second attempt is most easily made*!

If you want to go for it, go for it while you are still excited

– in other words, well before you get all the way down to the bottom of the mountain. Ask your man to pleasure you – or if he won't wake up, do it yourself.

In fact, you may find it easiest to 'join the ranks of the multi-orgasmic' by practising by yourself to begin with. And when you've convinced yourself that you can do it, you can then translate your new self-knowledge into multiple climaxes with your man.

Bonne chance!

USE THE FAMOUS CAT – AND THE PUSSY

You'll improve your chances of having good (and, if you wish, repeated) orgasms *during intercourse* if you use positions that give the best opportunity for maximum stimulation of your clitoris.

As we've pointed out earlier in this book, ordinary intercourse does *not* stimulate your clitoris very well – if at all. That's why we recommend postures in which one or other of you can stroke the little *cli-cli* with the fingertips.

But there is one position in which the man's pelvic thrusts *do* press on the clitoris, and that's the famous 'CAT'. These initials stand for 'Coitally Adjusted Technique' (romantic, eh?).

CAT was invented in America in the early 1990s, and you can see it in Figure 9.1. The basic idea is simply that the gentleman must 'ride much higher' than he would in ordinary sex, so that his shoulders and his head are about six inches (15 cm) further up the bed than they would be in the missionary position.

The effect of this is that his penis doesn't go all the way into your vagina. Instead, the 'stem' or 'root' of it is pulled hard against the topmost part of your opening – and against your clitoris.

Fig. 9.1

Quite a lot of couples like CAT, especially in America, and many say that it makes it easier for the lady to come during intercourse.

The man too will have interesting and unusual sensations – though CAT isn't every chap's cup of tea, particularly as he can't thrust in very deeply!

You shouldn't find it too difficult to get into the CAT position; the trick is to ask your man *not* to take his weight on his elbows for once. Instead, he should just let his bulk 'slump' on your upper chest.

We hope you can stand this! From his point of view, the 'no-elbows' approach does usually mean that he can feel your breasts pressed very firmly against him, which is definitely a bonus for the average male.

Note: CAT most definitely doesn't guarantee you an orgasm, but it's well worth a try.

The PUSSY position

This is something we've invented ourselves, and it appears here for the first time! It's another position in which there is pressure on the clitoris, so that the woman's chances of climaxing – or at least of really enjoying herself – are a lot better than in 'standard' postures.

PUSSY is basically like CAT upside-down. In order to try it out, get your man to lie flat on his back on the bed. Now lower yourself on to his penis, but only let it go *half-way in*.

Next, push your body well down the bed, so that your head is well below the level of his chin, and your hips are below his. The effect of this is to *bend* his cock slightly – and to jam the base of it firmly up against your clitoris. And away you go . . .

Incidentally, the acronym 'PUSSY' stands for Penis Underneath Scientifically Situated Yoni.

10

HOW TO GIVE WOMEN BETTER ORGASMS – A GUIDE FOR MEN

Yes – You *can* Help Her
Step One: Be Clean, Be Romantic – and Kiss Her!
Step Two: Take Your Time
Step Three: Keep an Eye on Her Calendar
Step Four: Compliment Her – Especially on Her Vulva
Step Five: Consider the 'Ladies Come First' Rule
Step Six: Use 'Dual Stimulation'
Step Seven: Master Finger Techniques
Step Eight: Master Oral Techniques
Step Nine: Learn How To Use a Vibrator on Her
Step Ten: Let Her Help Herself!
Step Eleven: Have Days When You're Her 'Sex Slave'
Step Twelve: Giving Her Multiple Orgasms

YES, YOU *CAN* HELP HER

A lot of guys still have the crazy idea that women are either highly orgasmic, or they aren't. And they imagine that there's nothing a man can do about it.

Nonsense! We can assure you that it's perfectly possible for a loving and enthusiastic chap to give his lady:

* more orgasms;
* better orgasms;
* multiple orgasms – if she wants them.

And all of this can be achieved *not* by the length of his penis or the force with which he thrusts it in, but instead by learning and using the simple tricks which we will outline in the next few pages. Please read on . . .

STEP ONE: BE CLEAN, BE ROMANTIC – AND KISS HER!

Before you start even thinking about sexual techniques, you've got to get prepared. And there are *three* preparatory things we'd like to suggest here:

* be clean;
* be romantic;
* kiss her a lot.

Be clean

This is absolutely vital. If you want to turn your woman on, you must make sure that your body is clean, and doesn't smell unpleasant. In particular, your hands and your penis *must* be clean. To try to make love to a lady when your fingers, fingernails or cock are dirty is not only crass, but also very unhygienic.

Curiously, when we try to mention this fact in print, it is often deleted by (male) editors! Yet women regularly write to us complaining that the bedroom hygiene of their menfolk makes it almost impossible for them to orgasm . . .

Be romantic

Women are not machines. If you don't understand that they need romance, affirmation, cuddles and loving, then there's no point in your reading the rest of this chapter.

Kiss her

Women correspondents endlessly complain to us that guys don't bother to kiss them – especially on the mouth. So don't omit this, fellas!

Incidentally, some of our female readers voice an alternative complaint: 'My man only kisses me on the mouth *when he wants sex.*' Do not fall into this trap. If you only kiss your partner in the bedroom – or when you're trying to get her into it – then she is likely to feel that you regard kissing her as just a way of persuading her to 'drop her pants'.

Please remember that to most women (and many men), kissing is a gentle romantic thing – an affirmation of love, rather than a demand for intercourse.

STEP TWO: TAKE YOUR TIME

As part of our survey, we asked women respondents to put on paper *the advice which they would give to men who want to help their partners reach orgasm.*

We were snowed under with replies which read '*tell them*

to take their time'.

Yes, women went on and on about how males want to take things far too quickly. What they would like you to do, gentlemen, is to slow right down!

So do not try to hurry your partner towards her orgasm (or her second orgasm, or her third . . .) — let her go at her own pace.

Bear in mind that that pace is almost certainly far, far slower than yours. A recent survey in *Cosmopolitan* showed that the average American woman would like anything from fifteen to forty-five minutes before she starts thinking seriously about orgasm.

And that is *not* some American affectation: much the same is true all over the world. For instance, in Scotland it's been shown that the average sexually active woman would prefer a good *hour* of love-play from you, if she could get it. So, take it easy . . .

STEP THREE: KEEP AN EYE ON HER CALENDAR

A high proportion of women have varying sexual desires – and therefore varying capacities for orgasm – at different times of their 'month'.

As we explain elsewhere in the book our survey shows that some females are at their sexiest halfway between periods, others are raunchiest just before menstruation, and some are actually very keen *during* the time of the period.

Admittedly, other women notice no particular variation, especially if they are over the age of fifty.

But what all this adds up to is that if you love the woman in your life, and want her to have the best orgasms, it's a good idea to be aware of her monthly changes of mood – and perhaps note down in your diary the dates when she's most likely to be orgasmic.

Then: seize the day!

STEP FOUR: COMPLIMENT HER – ESPECIALLY ON HER VULVA

Few men realise this, but most women feel uncertain or diffident about some aspect of their bodies. *This can cripple their ability to climax.*

In particular, a remarkable number of women have quite bad feelings about the vulva and vagina. Extraordinary as it may seem to you, it's very common for a female to feel that her pussy looks awful and doesn't smell very nice!

So you'll do her 'orgasmic confidence' a heck of a lot of good if you remember to compliment her on what great shape she's in.

In particular, praise the bits of her that she's likely to feel uncertain about. Our researches show that these are her:

- tummy;
- thighs;
- breasts;
- bottom;
- vulva and vagina.

Reassuring her that her vulva looks lovely – and smells and tastes nice – may well do wonders for her.

STEP FIVE: CONSIDER THE 'LADIES COME FIRST' RULE

A recent paper in an American medical journal described a

new approach to the eternal problem of trying to match the orgasmic needs of women with those of men. What the authors had done was simply to persuade a number of American couples to reach a mutual agreement that during their love-making sessions, the man would make sure *that the woman always came first.*

This 'ladies-first' approach seems to have worked quite well for some people. And it certainly avoided the constant difficulty (about which so many of our female readers complain) of the man having his orgasm first – and then falling asleep!

We don't say that the new American method is right for everyone, and we certainly don't think that you should use it every time. But we do think that there will be occasions where you could usefully tell your female partner: 'I'm in no rush at all, honey. Tonight, you come first . . .'

STEP SIX: USE 'DUAL STIMULATION'

As we discussed on page 195, *Cosmopolitan* magazine made a startling discovery at the beginning of the 1990s when its survey of a huge number of women revealed that for two-thirds of them, the most efficient way of getting an orgasm is to have 'dual stimulation'.

No, this doesn't mean that you have to get your best friend to drop in and help you in the bedroom. What it means is that you will probably get the best orgasmic results if you take care – on some occasions – to stimulate her in these two ways *at the same time*:

- clitorally;
- vaginally.

Please try and take this one on board, because it's very important. When the opportunity arises, just try the effect of caressing both clitoris *and* vagina simultaneously. It's tricky at first, but with practice, you can use your fingers, lips or tongue to achieve it very successfully.

STEP SEVEN: MASTER FINGER TECHNIQUES

But to give any kind of effective stimulation to the woman you love, and to bring her to orgasm with any regularity, you have to make yourself skilled at the main 'finger techniques' of love play. We've written extensively about these in our other books, but broadly speaking, they fall into two groups:

* finger techniques on her clitoris;
* finger techniques on her vagina.

Clitoris techniques

These are mainly carried out with the 'pads' of the first and second fingers of your dominant hand. If you look back at Figure 1.3 in Chapter One (page41), you'll see how they're applied.

We stress again that the vital thing is to let your partner guide you according to what *she* wants, but it's a good idea to cultivate the ability to move those fingerpads *very fast indeed*.

Vagina techniques

As we explained back in Chapter One, we think that it's very important to use your fingers to stretch the 'S-zone' of her vagina, which is packed with erotic nerve endings. Also, just try putting one or two well-lubricated fingers inside – and moving them in and out. This is a very simple caress, which often leads to orgasm; yet our researches show that many women report that no one has ever tried it on them.

STEP EIGHT: MASTER ORAL TECHNIQUES

A lot of women say that a fairly sure way to a good orgasm is to have cunnilingus from a man who really knows how to do it. And we would add that it is particularly effective if you make it part of 'dual stimulation' – please see page 209.

Anyway, it's quite clear that if you want to help your lady to lots and lots of nice climaxes, what you need to do is to make yourself a *master* of cunnilingus!

To be honest, this is about as difficult as becoming a Black Belt at Judo; however, if you're willing to work at it, you can make yourself pretty competent within a few weeks or so – *provided* that you *listen* to your partner, and do precisely what she wants you to do with your tongue and your lips.

In fact, that's the most important thing to learn about 'muff diving' – that you do what she asks for *not* what you think she should have . . .

STEP NINE: LEARN HOW TO USE A VIBRATOR ON HER

A vibrator isn't a sort of magic wand which will *automatically* give your loved one more and better orgasms, but it can help a lot.

So, if she hasn't already got one, buy one for her. (Do *not* produce one which you used on some previous lover: this is the height of sexual bad manners!) We strongly advise you not to succumb to the well-known male tendency to purchase the biggest one available. In general, females are more likely to respond to a small, non-threatening one. If it's compact enough for her to pack it discreetly in her hand-luggage when she goes on holiday, so much the better.

We've explained the use of vibrators earlier in this book –

see in particular Figure 1.4. We'd recommend that you concentrate on using the device in the area of her clitoris – only putting it inside if she asks you to. Please resist the common male temptation to shove the vibrator (jolly heartily) up the lady's vagina as though it were a substitute penis. You'll get much better results if you move it around very gently in the region of her pubic hair and clitoris.

Vibrators are especially good in two ways:

- for strengthening female orgasms. If a woman is just about to reach a climax caused by frigging, or by cunnilingus, or indeed by intercourse, then the judicious application of her vibrator to a sensitive part of her body during the last few seconds will often make the orgasm more intense for her.
- helping her to repeat the orgasm. If shortly after she's come, you gently and lovingly apply a vibrator to her clitoral area, this will often help her to climax again. See the section on multiple orgasms at the end of this chapter.

STEP TEN: LET HER HELP HERSELF!

As you may have discovered elsewhere in this book, we're strong advocates of the idea that women should feel free to 'touch themselves up' as a part of love-play.

This is certainly a trend which is spreading in this *fin de siècle* era of sexual openness: most of the women who we surveyed do masturbate – and most of those who masturbate say that they will sometimes do it with their partners there.

Though most males are very aroused by the idea of women frigging themselves, a few can't cope with it. If *you* find it difficult to accept, we ask you to consider some advantages of regularly letting your partner 'lend a hand':

- when you are literally doing everything you can to her (perhaps with your hands, mouth and penis fully occupied), the addition of her Flying Forefinger can be just the thing to boost her orgasm to even higher levels of pleasure;

- when you've just made her come – and have maybe come yourself – and you are lying there trying to recover your strength, it could well be that she is still highly excited. If so, a quick burst from her feminine fingers is a pretty sure route to multiple orgasms (see page 214).

STEP ELEVEN: HAVE DAYS WHEN YOU'RE HER 'SEX SLAVE'

It's an unfortunate fact that in many relationships, it's the man who 'sets the agenda' for love-making sessions. In other words, he tends to be the one who suggests (or even possibly dictates!) what position the couple move into next, and what kind of love-play activity they go in for.

This is not only pretty sexist, but it's also pretty counter-productive where generating female orgasms is concerned. After all, think of it the other way round: you probably wouldn't have a great time in bed if somebody was always saying to you 'Now you're going to lie on your back . . . next we'll do the sixty-nine . . . Do pay attention, dear, it's finger-frigging time . . .'

We jest . . . but it is true that many men are a bit too bossy in the sack! So as a counterbalance to any such tendency in your relationship, we suggest that you have evenings where *she* calls the shots – with the principal objective of giving her maximum orgasmic pleasure and as many orgasms as she wants.

On such nights, your basic aim should be to get her to 'use' you in any way that she wishes, purely for her own enjoyment. Have fun.

STEP TWELVE: GIVING HER MULTIPLE ORGASMS

If you are loving, understanding and considerate, and if you follow the eleven tips which we've already outlined, then you'll stand an excellent chance of giving her multiple orgasms – and probably loads and loads of them.

Don't force her into them, but be open-minded to the fact that she may need many more than you suspected.

We offer you one tip in particular. **The time when a woman is most 'vulnerable' to having another orgasm is in the couple of minutes or so immediately after the previous one**. (How very different from ourselves, dear gentlemen readers!)

The reasons for this phenomenon are explained elsewhere in this book. And if you make use of it, you will give your partner many happy and delightful *multiple* orgasms.

PART TWO

Men's Orgasms

11

WHAT HAPPENS TO A MAN'S BODY AT ORGASM

The Myth • The Reality • How Climaxes Happen in Men •
What Is the Fluid? • What Makes it Spurt Out? • 'Pre-Come'
Fluid: a Warning • Ten Methods of Reaching a Climax • Wet
Dreams • Masturbation • Hand Petting • Fellatio • Sexual
Intercourse • Dry Orgasms • How Long Do Males Take To
Reach Orgasm? • How Often Do Men Have Orgasms? •
How Orgasms Change Through Life • Multiple Climaxes in
Men • Faking Male Orgasm

THE MYTH

❛Between the rose-pink lips of Mary's hungry vaginal opening, Tom's long, rock-hard penis was thrusting faster and faster. As his rhythm quickened, the bursting, purple head of his lusty organ penetrated ever deeper into her, till it seemed to both of them that no man on Earth had ever been so far inside a woman.

Now his harsh breaths came more and more rapidly, as he sensed that his climax was almost upon him. Finally, one wild breath ripped out of him in a mighty groan as he slammed his pelvis hard against hers, grinding desperately into her pubic hair.

He heard Mary's responding scream fill his ears as the fierce contractions in the base of his organ began,.He knew that he was pumping jet after jet of precious love-fluid into the warm depths of her welcoming opening. It seemed to him that he was drenching the inside of her body with the sheer torrent of his lust – and he *knew* that she could feel the fountain of white liquid squirting out of him and up into her womb.

Throb after throb now shook his loins, till at last he began to subside into a blessed unconsciousness – an unconsciousness in which he was still aware of seeing fireworks exploding in the sky, to the sound of heavenly trumpets.

Naturally, ten minutes later he was ramrod-stiff again, and ready for more action. "Wake up, my darling," he murmured, "I *must* have you one more time . . ."❜

THE REALITY

Now what you've just read is the picture of male orgasm which is painted by countless erotic novels and men's magazines! Even males who've never read such publications seem to believe that this is how it should be – all the time. The story which we've told you embodies every favourite masculine fantasy, such as the following:

- the man's penis must be very, very *long* by the time he 'comes';
- it must also be astoundingly *hard*;
- As the 'Big O' approaches, he must thrust his organ incredibly deeply into the woman;
- she must climax *simultaneously* with him;
- he must pump *gallons* of love-juice far into her gynaecological regions;
- she must *feel* it squirting around her 'insides';
- his body should *throb* uncontrollably ('throbbing' is very big in male mythology . . .);
- he should see exploding lights – and then virtually pass out cold;
- most importantly, he should be ready for another orgasm almost immediately – because, of course, a really 'virile' guy can do it again and again all night!

Now to be fair, the scenario which we've provided you with does genuinely contain some elements of reality. Yes, a really good male orgasm can sometimes be not all that far off what we have described, even though *some* things in our mythical story are completely impossible. For instance:

- men do not pump 'gallons' of love-juice into women; the average per climax is only about a teaspoon (5 ml or 5 cc), something many males find very difficult to accept!
- women *cannot* feel blokes ejaculating inside them. All that

stuff in stories about how 'Felicia felt the dewy warmth of Jasper's hot male liquid shooting up into the far recesses of her internal organs' is sheer baloney.

• hardly any men (though there are a few exceptions, as we'll see shortly) can make love again after a climax – at least, not until they've had a nice, long rest!

So a more accurate account of a fairly common sort of male orgasm might be something like this:

❛After around ten minutes of intercourse, Jim was feeling a bit worried about his erection. How he wished he hadn't had that third pint of beer!

Fortunately, Suzie now whispered something *extremely* rude in his ear, and that galvanised him. Galvanised him a bit too much, in fact – because he suddenly realised that he was about to climax, and that nothing could stop it.

"Oh God, oh God," he moaned. "I'm coming! I'm coming!"

"Gosh, not *already* darling," said Suzie crossly. "Can't you just keep going a bit longer? I need at least another five minutes."

But it was too late. "Sorry," gasped Jim, feeling that the edge had rather been taken off his enjoyment because of what he regarded as Suzie's decidedly selfish remark. The "pumping" feeling definitely wasn't as good as he'd have liked . . .

He tried to give a few more thrusts, but found it almost impossible because his penis had already lost a lot of its erection and was threatening to fall out. What's more – as often happened after an orgasm – it was feeling rather *sensitive*, as though it didn't want to be touched . . .

"Sorry," he said again thickly, and then fell deeply asleep on top of The Woman He Loved.

Lying flat on her back in the dark, Suzie thought

briefly about "frigging" herself but then decided that she couldn't quite manage to get her right hand under the weight of Jim's inert body.

"Oh gosh," she thought suddenly. "Did I remember to take the bloody Pill?"❯

HOW CLIMAXES HAPPEN IN MEN

OK, so what basically *does* happen in a man's body during a climax?

Well, let's start by having a quick look at some of the factors that help make men reach orgasm. You'll see that they include:

- friction on the skin of the 'shaft' of the penis;
- friction on its tip;
- stimulation of other erotically sensitive areas of the body, such as the scrotum, the nipples, the lips, the buttocks, and (in quite a lot of men) the anus;
- erotic sights, smells and sounds;
- erotic thoughts in his brain.

If you're a woman, then perhaps the most important thing for you to realise is that it's friction on the shaft of his 'cock' which is far and away the most significant factor in making a chap climax. It's almost impossible for the average guy to reach orgasm *unless* he gets that friction – which is, of course, most commonly caused by somebody's fingers, or by the walls of your vagina.

Whichever way it is caused, this agreeable friction stimulates 'pleasure receptors' in the skin which covers the shaft of your man's penis. These receptors send nerve impulses up to the erotic nerve centres in the spinal cord and brain.

Now once those centres have been sufficiently stimulated by the bombardment of impulses arriving from the penis, they suddenly fire off a *tremendous* nervous discharge – rather as if the bloke were having a gloriously pleasurable sneeze, in fact.

This wild nerve discharge now sweeps rapidly down to his sex organs, where it triggers off an uncontrollable squirting of fluid from the tip of his penis.

Additional factors that help make him come

Though we've said that it's basically friction on the shaft of his penis that makes a man climax, the other factors listed on page 222 do play a big part.

Stroking or kissing or licking the *tip* of his organ, or his nipples, or any of the other erotically sensitive areas of his body, may help tip him over the edge. (Indeed, a very few men say that they can climax through nipple-stroking alone, as we'll see shortly.)

What a guy sees and smells and hears may also help make him come. For instance, any male teenager will tell you that he climaxes a lot quicker if he's looking at a photo of a beautiful woman. In the masturbatory races which go on quite frequently in this age group, participants soon discover that they will reach the 'finishing line' more quickly if someone helpfully shouts out the word 'breasts'.

Similarly, a lot of males will reach orgasm faster if they can smell female perspiration – or indeed vaginal secretions. And if your man hears you whisper something sexy and exciting in his ear while he's making love to you, that may well make him fire off.

For women readers, there's a clear message here; it's great to turn your partner on, of course, but if you don't want him to climax too soon, then do take it a bit easy with these 'accessory' methods of triggering orgasm.

And if he's grimly trying not to go over the top, beware of

putting your finger on his bottom and shrieking 'Fuck me, darling'!

There's such a thing as the last straw, you know . . .

WHAT IS THE FLUID?

The white, sticky, vanilla-scented fluid which men pump out at the moment of orgasm contains an almost unbelievable number of sperms – often as many as 400 million in one climax.

But sperms, which are very tiny indeed, only make up a minute proportion of this fluid. Most of it actually comes from the prostate gland and from other structures like the *seminal vesicles* which (as you'll see from Figure 11.2) are located along the tubing which leads from the man's testicles up to his penis.

To be honest, doctors are still not very sure about what all these structures actually *do*! They certainly contribute to the sheer bulk of the ejaculate, and maybe they help to nourish the sperm, but who knows?

However, from a sexual/erotic point of view, it may be worth knowing that if the woman stimulates structures like the prostate and the seminal vesicles (in ways which are described later in this book), certain remarkable things can happen:

• the man may well find it easier to come;
• his pleasure may be intensified;
• the volume of fluid will probably increase;
• the sex fluid will probably shoot a good deal further!

No wonder that ladies like Heidi Fleiss – the world-famous 'Hollywood Hooker' – appear to have been able to found a successful career on the art of prostate massage . . .

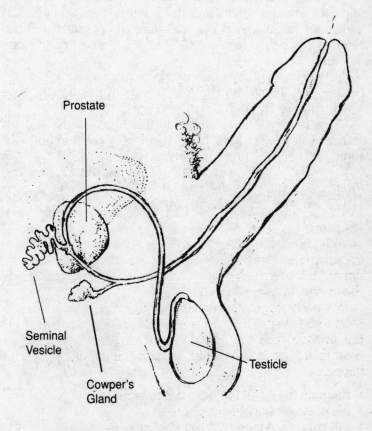

Prostate

Seminal
Vesicle

Cowper's
Gland

Testicle

Fig. 11.2

WHAT MAKES IT SPURT OUT?

As we said a moment ago, a massive discharge of nerve impulses sweeps down from the brain and spinal cord and makes all these sexual glands – like the prostate and the seminal vesicles – pour out their juices at exactly the same moment.

But where are they poured *into*? Figure 11.3 makes this clear – they flood into the lowest part of the narrow pipe which runs up through the man's penis.

There is *very* little room inside this tube. So the sudden arrival of all this sex fluid 'blows it out' very considerably – to about two or three times its normal width.

The more it is distended the greater the man's pleasure. (Many guys will tell you that really good orgasms are often associated with large volumes of 'spunk'.)

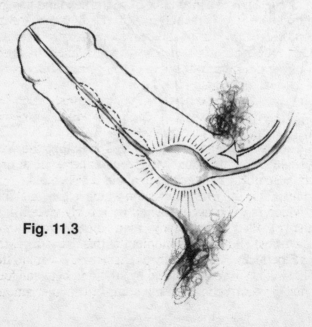

Fig. 11.3

The fraction of a second when all the liquid comes gushing into the base of the pipe is what American sexologists rather grandly call 'the moment of ejaculatory inevitability'. In other words, it's the moment when the man knows that virtually nothing on earth will stop him coming.

And we really do mean 'virtually nothing'. At that moment, you could point a gun at a chap's head, or tell him his house was on fire, or congratulate him on winning the Irish Sweepstake; none of it would make any difference – he would still have the orgasm.

Indeed in a case which we investigated, a middle-aged gentleman was about to reach his climax inside a young lady of 'easy virtue' when Scotland Yard's Vice Squad broke down the bedroom door. The client was completely unable to stop, and the police very decently waited until he had finished before arresting him. We feel that this story lends new meaning to the phrase 'the customer always comes first . . .'

Why is ejaculation inevitable once the sex fluid has gushed into the pipe? It's partly because there's nowhere for it to go except out of the tip of the penis, and partly because the tremendous 'blast' of nerve activity which happens at orgasm makes the muscular walls of the little pipe *contract repeatedly and with very great force.*

Men can feel these powerful contractions, which happen at intervals of about 0.8 of a second, and which are associated with very great pleasure indeed.

If you're a woman, you may well feel that they're very similar to the contractions which *you* experience at orgasm, which also occur at intervals of about 0.8 seconds.

In men, it is the *first* contraction which is the most intense, and which is often accompanied by a fairly violent forward thrust of the body. Many men moan, gasp or even (sometimes) shout at the moment of this first surge, though few of them cry out as loudly as the average woman does.

That initial surge is followed by anything between four and ten further contractions, which pump out smaller amounts of fluid. However, any male will tell you that each contraction is very pleasurable. Many men 'twitch' their pelvic muscles, often without really knowing they're doing it, in time with the contractions, in order to 'help' the spunk out, and indeed to increase the pleasant feelings.

So strong are the early contractions that when the fluid comes spurting out of the end of the man's penis, it will usually shoot some distance. Even if the orgasm isn't particularly earth-shattering, the liquid may well jet a couple of inches (5 cm) upwards.

But if it's what some people call a 'super-orgasm', then the sex fluid can sometimes achieve the remarkable feat of leaping about A YARD (roughly a metre) from the end of the man's cock. For instance, a highly charged young lad who has had a really great orgasm after a period of sexual abstinence may well find that it finishes up in his hair, or his partner's . . .

'PRE-COME' FLUID: A WARNING

Very often it's the case that *before* the man comes, a certain amount of fluid appears at the tip of his organ – usually just a few drops, but more if he's been sexually excited for a long time. This is widely known as 'pre-come'.

It isn't the same as seminal fluid. For a start, it's clear, rather than white. And it has no real taste (in contrast to the rather salty/bitter tang of spunk).

Nobody is quite sure where it originates from, but some sexologists have said that it comes from little structures called 'Cowper's glands', which you can see in Figure 11.2. We think it's more likely that it comes partly from the prostate gland , because if a woman massages a man's prostate region with her finger, that certainly makes it flow.

But the really important thing you need to know about pre-come fluid is this. *It frequently contains sperms.*

That's why the very common practice of beginning intercourse without a condom – in other words, just putting it on halfway through – is dangerous. If a couple do this, the guy's pre-come may get the woman pregnant.

Incidentally, pre-come causes the silvery stains which so many males find inside the fronts of their underpants. Boys and young men tend to worry about these marks, and to think that they may be suffering from a discharge. Indeed, Pakistani and Indian chaps often write to us because they wrongly fear that the fluid loss may weaken them, or damage their health. This is because of the age-old South Asian belief that losing sperm means losing part of your life force.

However, the production of pre-come is just the male body's normal reaction to (say) an evening's snogging, or thinking a few sexy thoughts, or even just seeing a pretty woman.

TEN METHODS OF REACHING A CLIMAX

There are ten ways in which males reach climaxes. If you're a man, you're probably aware of nearly all of them, but if you're a woman you may be slightly surprised by what follows . . .

The five ways in which heterosexual males most *commonly* achieve orgasm are:

- wet dreams;
- masturbation;
- hand-petting;
- oral sex (fellatio);
- sexual intercourse.

We'll look in more detail at the 'Big Five' in a minute. But there are five other ways in which males *sometimes* have climaxes. Here they are:

- spontaneous orgasms;
- 'frotting' orgasms;
- nipple orgasms;
- accidental orgasms;
- orgasms from rectal intercourse.

Spontaneous orgasms

It's actually possible for men to have spontaneous orgasms (in other words, ones that just happen – out of the blue), though these are rare.

They're commonest in teenage boys, and may occur while simply *thinking* about women or sex. But scientific authorities agree that, bizarre as it may seem, they do occasionally happen when the chap's mind is very far from thoughts of sexual matters.

You would be right in supposing that it must be extremely embarrassing for a young man if he has a climax while just walking down the street! In practice, it seems that these spontaneous orgasms are most liable to happen under conditions of great mental tension – for instance, while giving a public performance on stage, or even while fighting in a battle.

'Frotting' orgasms

'Frotting' means 'rubbing', and quite a lot of orgasms in young males come from rubbing the penis against something – which could be a material (e.g., bed linen) or a person. Men will often climax as a result of friction against a partner's breasts, thighs or tummy, or indeed *any* part of a woman's body. Females are often quite surprised that an excited male can very easily get sexual satisfaction from every nook, cranny or surface of the feminine form.

(Incidentally, a *frotteur* is one of those rather ghastly fellows who get their kicks by rubbing against women in buses, trains or lifts.)

Nipple orgasms

Although quite a substantial minority of women can reach 'the Big O' just through having their nipples fondled, it is a rare ability among males.

However, in our researches we have heard from men who claim quite convincingly that nipple stimulation 'fetches them off'. One man's letter read:

> Since my teenage years I have known that if I was sexually excited and wanted to relieve my frustration, all I had to do was to lie down and stroke my nipples for a few minutes. Even today, if a loving woman does this to me in bed, it will rapidly make me spurt.

Accidental orgasms

Women readers may be taken aback to hear that highly sexed young men quite often have *accidental* orgasms, probably caused by a combination of a spot of friction on the penis plus a certain amount of erotic thought, which the unfortunate lad may be trying desperately to suppress!

The classic case is that of the poor young devil who goes to an old-fashioned ball in a posh suit, and finds himself doing a 'close-together' dance with an attractive girl. The pressure of her body against his loins – together with the sight and smell of her – causes first of all an involuntary erection, and then, despite all his efforts to prevent it, an embarrassing ejaculation. Most etiquette books are silent on the subject of how to cover up a damp patch which is spreading inexorably across the front of your tuxedo trousers.

If in doubt, just dangle a large table-napkin or handkerchief in front of yourself . . .

Orgasms from rectal intercourse

You may be surprised to learn that these are *not* confined to gay chaps! We don't recommend rectal intercourse, partly because it carries certain health risks and partly because it is actually *illegal* – even between husband and wife – in many countries.

But facts must be faced, and the truth is that many orgasms *do* come from rectal sex. The highly authoritative British Wellcome survey (one of the most comprehensive studies published in the 1990s) has found that more than one in eight men and women have gone in for anal intercourse.

One astonishing finding of the Wellcome survey is the fact that rectal sex is actually much commoner among the working classes! If you're a working man or woman, you're twice as likely as a 'posh' person to have had 'bottom sex' in the last year.

Incidentally, this is in sharp contrast to the situation with *oral* sex, which is far more popular among the upper classes! Neither of these remarkable findings has received any publicity so far, mainly (we presume) because of the fact that people think it's politically incorrect to mention 'class' these days . . .

Male orgasms from rectal intercourse are sometimes said to be fairly intense by those who have tried this activity. This is because the 'sphincter' muscle surrounding the opening of the bottom is very, very *tight* compared with the vagina. However, many people – and especially women! – find rectal sex pretty uncomfortable, simply because that particular opening is small and, unlike the vagina, has no natural lubrication to help matters along. (Not surprisingly, damage to the tight anal ring is common.)

We should add that a few men report that they can orgasm through being on the 'receiving end' (so to speak) of rectal intercourse. These orgasms are probably, at least in part, connected with stimulation of the prostate gland.

Now to look at the Big Five.

WET DREAMS

Researchers say that 83 per cent of all males have wet dreams (politely known as 'nocturnal emissions') at some time in their lives. If you don't know what a wet dream is, it's one in which the guy reaches orgasm while fast asleep. Often, he may be unable to recall any dream at all, but simply wakes up with clear evidence of orgasm – such as a damp patch on the sheets, or dried semen on the lower part of his belly.

However, in most cases the male has a clear recollection of an extremely sexy dream, in which all sorts of jolly things happened! Understandably, naked and nubile ladies frequently feature in the scenario. In many cases, the dream ends with the orgasm – at which point the sleeper may wake up.

The climax which happens during a wet dream isn't usually of immense intensity, but it is generally pleasurable. Unfortunately, in a few cases the dream may involve all sorts of disturbing things (like sex with a relative, or another man, or other 'forbidden' people), and in these instances the orgasm isn't likely to be very thrilling, and may well be followed by feelings of guilt. These are really quite unnecessary, because no one can help what they dream!

But, in most cases, a nocturnal emission is a thoroughly pleasant experience, and one which is clearly Nature's way of 'letting off steam'.

There's tremendous variation in how often males climax during their sleep. About 17 per cent of men appear *never* to ejaculate in their dreams. On the other hand, a small group of males claim to do it almost every time they awaken from sleeping, which certainly must make nodding off while on the top of a bus into a somewhat perilous experience . . .

Nocturnal orgasms occur most frequently in the young. Research suggests that most teenage boys will have them once or twice a month, but there is no doubt that some highly sexed youths will have several per week. That often causes them considerable embarrassment, particularly if they are producing considerable volumes of fluid and staining the family sheets! *It's important that parents should be understanding, and non-condemnatory, about this.*

When men settle down in marriage (or in co-habitation) these dreams tend to become much less frequent, for a fairly obvious reason: the chap is likely to be getting regular intercourse. It is said that after marriage, only 2 to 6 per cent of male orgasms happen through wet dreams.

In general, dream orgasms tend to become less frequent as a man grows older, though there are certainly men well over the age of fifty who have them.

What makes them happen?

They're probably in part due to the intense sexual excitement in the male's brain as he dreams of sexy things. And it's likely that another powerful factor is *friction* of the bedclothes or pyjamas against a highly engorged penis.

Most men's organs become erect a number of times each night while they are asleep, and it's almost inevitable that the swollen 'prick' will rub against something or other.

Indeed, if you want to give your partner an interesting and rather surprising orgasm, it's not a bad idea to take hold of his penis between finger and thumb when you notice that he's lying there fast asleep with a large erection. If you handle matters correctly, you may well give him very pleasant feelings, as well as a most enjoyable dream . . .

MASTURBATION

Next among the 'Big Five' is masturbation. Let's have no pussy-footing nonsense about whether masturbation is 'normal'. Of course it is!

Female readers may be interested to know that men masturbate even more frequently than women do. Every worthwhile sex survey carried out in the second half of the twentieth century has confirmed that the vast majority of males have masturbated – and indeed continue masturbating from time to time, even when they are in established sexual relationships.

For example, Shere Hite found in one of her American studies that out of all males who had sex two or three times a week with a female partner, no less than 79 per cent also 'jerked themselves off' at least once a week!

This certainly is an extraordinary testament to the average man's need for orgasm. Of course, we must make the point that there are males – particularly older ones – who rarely or never masturbate. On the other hand (if you'll forgive the phrase) we have taken evidence from one highly sexed British husband who, in addition to having regular and enthusiastic sex with his wife *and* carrying on unwise liaisons with four regular girlfriends, regarded it as perfectly reasonable to take home a nude pin-up magazine some nights 'for an early evening wank'. Furthermore, if life ever seemed a teeny bit dull to him, he would immediately ring up one of those 'telephone sex' services and spend a happy ten minutes rubbing himself to orgasm while the young woman on the other end of the line encouraged him . . .

We have noted one interesting trend in male masturbation during the last few years. Until quite recently, it would have been most unusual for a Western male to 'frig' himself *with his partner there.* But in today's freer climate – and perhaps encouraged by women's magazine pundits, who now tend to regard this kind of activity as 'therapeutic' – there are quite a lot of men who will masturbate while their female partner looks on.

The object of this exercise is often just to get a firmer erection, but it can be part of the couple's love-play, especially as there are quite a few women who are very turned on by the sight of a chap 'doing it to himself', even if he goes as far as climaxing.

Incidentally, it is worth a woman's while to be aware of *how* men masturbate to orgasm . The reason for this is simple: if you know the type of grip, speed, pressure and rhythm that he prefers, then it'll be much easier for you to give him pleasure when you handle him.

So what do men do? Ms Shere Hite, the definitive authority on this (as on so much else), found in her massive survey of American males that the following are their preferred techniques of self-masturbation:

82 %	By hand
15 %	Lying on tummy and simply pressing penis down on bed
.1 %	Grinding penis between legs
0.5 %	Massage with water spray
0.5 %	Self-fellatio (though we stress that this is onlyavailable to the tiny minority of men who are so flexible that they could probably make a living as contortionists!)
1 %	Never masturbate

Therefore as you can see, the great majority of males bring themselves to climax by using their hands. Our researches indicate that most of these chaps actually do it by

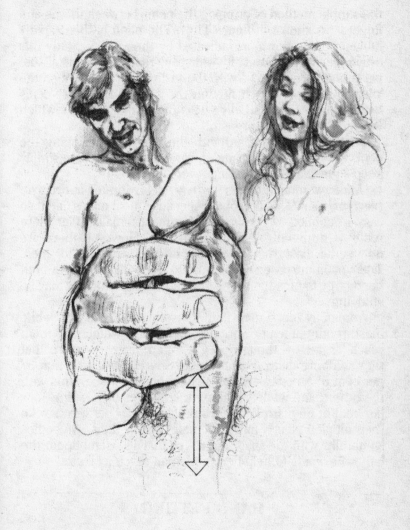

Fig. 11.4

the simple method of gripping the penis between thumb and fingers (as shown in figure 11.4). The hand is then rapidly moved up and down, as indicated by the arrows. Study this drawing, ma'am, and it will pay rich dividends! Take particular care to press with the pads of your fingers on the 'pleasure ridge', which lies on the side of the erect penis *away* from the man's belly – it is often this pressure which will help achieve the orgasm.

Other men masturbate with the whole fist gripping the penis (again, with an up-and-down movement). Some simply keep squeezing and relaxing.

Unlike women, men very *rarely* use a vibrator in order to reach orgasm. This is probably because most males find it so easy to climax, as compared with most females, that there really is no need for mechanical aids! However, there are now some masturbatory sex-aid devices available for men. Their main purpose seems to be to leave the gent with both hands free to turn the pages of whatever literature he may be studying . . .

Women readers may find it useful to know that while masturbating, men do various other things which help them reach orgasm – though they're often scarcely aware that they're doing them. For instance, Shere Hite found that 37 per cent of American males stroke their own scrotums with the other hand while 'touching themselves up'. Twenty-four per cent of men stroke their buttocks, and 7 per cent stroke their nipples. Nearly half of all males stroke their own bodies 'generally' with the spare hand – so that's a useful tip for the lady who wants to help her gentleman reach a climax.

HAND PETTING

Being 'hand-petted' or 'rubbed up' or 'tossed off' by a female partner is of course another very common way in which males reach a climax. A recently published major British survey suggested that 82 per cent of men had been stimulated in this way; indeed, more than a quarter of all had enjoyed the experience during the last week!

However, many couples don't pursue hand-petting to the point of orgasm, and on most occasions simply use it as a stage in an evening's love-play, or indeed as a way of helping the man get an erection.

If you *do* hand-pet all the way to climax, you have to decide what to do with the man's ejaculate! In bed there is no difficulty, and most couples will let it splash wherever it falls (the woman's bosom is a much-favoured site). But if you are petting elsewhere, it may be advisable to have a clean hanky or some tissues to catch the 'flood' . . .

The techniques of hand-petting are, as we've already said, best modelled on what a man does to himself while he's masturbating. However, women can do one or two things which are not easy for the male to do to himself. In particular, a woman can easily rub the *sides* of the erect penis and so bring her partner to climax.

All types of hand-petting are made rather easier (and are more likely to achieve results) if you use a little lubricant. To be frank, this is the reason why girls in topless massage parlours are invariably equipped with a tube of Baby Oil or (in America) Astroglide. Equally useful in the home is some talcum powder or face cream. And – though we hope this won't upset you – many uninhibited women cheerfully use their own saliva.

Bringing the man to orgasm through a 'hand-job' is not usually very difficult (except in cases of 'Ejaculatory Incompetence', please see Chapter Fourteen). Usually, firm pressure on the shaft of the penis – as shown in Figure 11.5 – coupled with very *rapid* rubbing, will do the trick.

Many males actually report that the orgasm which is reached in this way is more 'locally intense' than the one which they get from sexual intercourse.

Fig. 11.5

In other words, they say that in the hands of an experienced woman they get a tremendously strong sensation *in the penis itself* as the ejaculate is forced out – even though the emotional and romantic satisfaction may be much less than that achieved when making love.

The knowledge that 'a good jerk-off' gives more exquisite localised feelings than actual intercourse is very widespread among males. That's why many young men in certain Western cultures are familiar with a bar-room ditty (to the tune of *Funiculi, Funicula*) which goes:

> Sexual intercourse, of course, is absolutely grand;
> But for personal satisfaction, I prefer the hand.

Nevertheless . . . in our 1995 survey we have found that men prefer the *overall* experience of orgasm through intercourse to the experience of orgasming through a hand-job.

Almost three-quarters of all males said they preferred an 'intercourse orgasm' to a love-play one. This is an extraordinary contrast with women's attitudes – as we've seen earlier in this book, our survey shows that most women prefer love-play climaxes to intercourse ones.

FELLATIO

The fourth of the five common methods of reaching male orgasm is fellatio. This means oral sex, given to a man by a woman. And when we say 'oral sex', what we mean is:

- kissing the penis;
- licking the penis;
- sucking the penis.

Fig. 11.6

In practice, licking and kissing the 'cock' are *not* very likely to lead to orgasm by themselves, except in young and/or explosively triggered males. It is really sucking – using the technique shown in Figure 11.6 – which causes the great majority of oral sex climaxes.

Until quite recent years, fellatio was widely condemned by certain narrow-minded moralists, and indeed was sometimes referred to as a 'sexual perversion'. It was actually *illegal* under certain circumstances in some American states!

Such attitudes seem almost incredible nowadays, when fellatio has become a normal part of most younger couples' love-play – and when it is recognised by experts as a most valuable technique (especially when the male has difficulties with potency).

How common is it? Well, the definitive American survey of the 1990s, published by the University of Chicago, found that 27 per cent of American males had had it during the past year. The British Wellcome survey has recently discovered that *over two-thirds* of men have been on the receiving end of fellatio – and about two-thirds of all women have given it.

An extraordinary finding of the British survey (which has not, so far as we are aware, been reported in the press) is that it is the upper classes who are much more likely to have fellatio! Better-off and better-educated women are the ones who are the most willing to offer it to their menfolk.

In fact, this remarkable discovery does fit in very well with Dr Kinsey's report of many years ago that it was *college-educated* U.S. males and females who were keenest on fellatio.

The technique of 'fellating' a man is really quite difficult, and to be frank it takes a lot of practice to become very good at it. Our advice to women readers is to ask the man what he likes best and then do it – provided that *you* feel comfortable with it.

You will probably find it helpful to combine the sucking and kissing and licking with simultaneous 'hand massage' of your partner's penis. Putting your hand on his shaft also helps you to control the depth of his penetration – an important point, since many women dislike deep thrusting. (Unfortunately, this is what many men adore.)

Do you take fellatio all the way to orgasm? Many couples don't, and simply use it for a minute or two before going on to something else.

However, if you do go all the way then you have to face the very tricky question of what to do with his ejaculate when he climaxes. Since the mid-1990s, women's magazines have devoted a lot of space to the great 'Should Women Swallow?' controversy. We do not propose to offer an opinion on this point of etiquette, but we would draw your attention to two facts:

• if you are a man, you should realise that some women are really disgusted by the idea of someone coming in their mouths;
• If you're a woman, it's as well to bear in mind that a majority of males (55 per cent in one recent survey) not only want to ejaculate in a partner's mouth, but also wish to see her swallow the liquid.

If there is a divergence of opinions between the two of you on this subject, a common compromise is for the lady to remove the penis from her mouth at the last second, so that the ejaculation occurs outside.

But if it occurs *inside,* what sensations does this produce in the man? Very nice ones, of course, but also very variable ones, since they depend very much on the woman's skill at fellatio, and also on just which structures (tongue, cheek or lips) are creating the major pressure on his organ at the moment of climax.

One thing to avoid at all costs is pressure with the *teeth*, which has ruined many a good orgasm!

The pressure exerted by the female's lips is not usually as great as that exerted by the vagina. This is probably the reason why many men will rather reluctantly admit that this exotic and exciting way of having sex doesn't really give them quite as good orgasms as sexual intercourse does. Indeed, our survey shows that most males – not all – do prefer the sensation of coming in the vagina to that of coming in the mouth.

Research published in 1994 suggested that a lot of men do actually find it quite difficult to reach orgasm while in their partner's mouth, no matter how attractive they may find the idea. So they tend to enjoy being fellated for a little while before climaxing in some other way. It's noteworthy that in America, Shere Hite found that over 40 per cent of her male 'subjects' rarely or never ejaculated while being sucked.

In sharp contrast, we have noticed a recent trend among young women to *encourage* their male partners to orgasm in the mouth. This vogue seems to have arisen in University circles, where female students use the method as a way of avoiding having full sex.

One young Cambridge student explained to us: 'It avoids a lot of hassle if you just suck a man off fairly early in the proceedings. Then he just goes to sleep and you don't have to have intercourse with him.'

Note: Although many people regard fellatio as a 'low-risk activity' for HIV infection, we think that it is always best to exercise caution. In our view, it is absolutely crazy to let casual acquaintances ejaculate inside you. (This applies to intercourse as well as oral sex.) Even in a regular relationship, a woman should consider insisting on using a condom unless she is completely sure that the man is HIV-negative.

SEXUAL INTERCOURSE

The last of the 'Big Five' ways of reaching orgasm is of course sexual intercourse. In fact, this is the commonest way of climaxing for most adult males (though not for teenagers, in whom masturbation orgasms are more common).

In our survey about 85 per cent of men report that they have climaxed in this way during the past year; the figures for oral sex, hand-petting and masturbation are very much lower – though it's important to realise that many males regularly engage in *all* these ways of reaching a climax. The old belief that men should only reach orgasm through intercourse is, of course, nonsense.

We don't think that there's any need to tell our readers *how* to have an orgasm during sexual intercourse – because the fact is that it is incredibly easy. The problem for most men is to *avoid* reaching it too quickly, and we'll be dealing with that shortly.

But it's worth considering *why* sexual intercourse so readily leads to male orgasm (a stark contrast with *female* orgasm, which is not all that easily induced by intercourse alone). Firstly there are various 'ancillary factors' which tend to make a man come very readily during vaginal intercourse. They include the following:

- the tremendous emotional charge which a man gets from knowing that his organ is inside the most intimate place in an attractive woman's body;
- the powerful romantic feelings which arise from being so closely entwined with someone who (we hope!) he loves;
- the warmth and softness of a woman's body pressed against his own;
- the feel of her 'secondary sexual characteristics', like her breasts and buttocks – though in fact, it's a curious quirk of Nature that in the most common position of intercourse

(the 'missionary'), the man can't easily feel or see the woman's breasts;
- the terrific stimulation of feeling her mouth on his – because in the majority of intercourse positions, the couple can kiss each other;
- the stimulus of her bodily smells (particularly from her vagina); some of these scents, called 'pheromones', are actually perceived at an unconscious level – so that the man isn't actually aware that he is smelling them;
- the sight of her, particularly as she becomes sexually excited – sexual arousal makes women's eyes, pupils and breasts bigger, as well as giving them an attractive flush (though this last feature is only seen in fair-skinned women);
- the *sounds* she makes are also highly erotic and help to drive the man toward orgasm – we don't just mean what she says, but also the sound of her rapid breathing, which is a real turn-on for most males; also if she happens to climax, then the noise of her shrieks will help to urge him on!

But . . . the *main* stimulus which drives a man to orgasm during sexual intercourse is quite simply the enormously agreeable pressure of her vagina on his penis. The word vagina is actually Latin for 'sheath', and (as you'll doubtless have noticed) the vagina really does fit round a man's organ with the most extraordinary snugness.

So as he thrusts in and out, the moist and cushioned walls of her vagina are in effect stroking up and down against the sides, front and back of his penis.

In particular, the tight ring of muscle which encircles the first three inches of the vagina makes a sort of 'collar' round his shaft. Being enclosed within this firm yet comforting circle is a powerful stimulus to orgasm.

If you're a woman, it's worth knowing that *tightness* is what men value very highly – though within reason, of course: an excessively tight vagina can be a cause of pain for both partners. (Over-tightness is usually due either to lack of preliminary love-play and romancing, or else to the very common female sexual difficulty called 'vaginismus', in which there is an involuntary contraction of the circular muscle whenever anyone makes an approach to the vagina; these days it can be successfully treated.)

A man can sometimes have problems in reaching orgasm if his partner's vaginal ring has become too slack – which is common after having had babies. This slackness may well make intercourse unsatisfactory for the woman too. The remedy is usually to do regular vaginal muscle exercises, but in some cases the woman may opt for having a 'tightening-up' operation by a gynaecologist.

So, tightness is a major factor in helping the man reach orgasm. Furthermore, many men say that a woman's tightness is of great help in improving the *quality* of the climax. Sexually experienced ladies are often well aware of this fact, and exploit it by *deliberately* contracting and relaxing their vaginal muscle as the gentleman reaches his 'peak'. We strongly recommend this technique!

Our researches suggest that another potent factor in causing male orgasm may be the strong pressure which the area round a woman's clitoris exerts on the lower part of her man's shaft.

That area of the female genitals is very *firm*, because her pubic bone lies behind it. So when a man gets his cock very deeply into her and 'grinds' hard against her vulva, then her bone is pressing strongly against the lowest inch or so of his prick – on the side which is nearer to his belly. The average man finds this sensation extraordinarily erotic, so it may well help to fire him off!

DRY ORGASMS

Although most male orgasms result in a highly satisfying squirt of fluid, some don't. The man comes, but no fluid emerges. Not surprisingly, this is described as a 'dry orgasm'.

This can be a bit alarming if it happens to you, but there's usually a simple explanation. Here are the main possibilities:

- a dry orgasm can occur if a male has already had several climaxes in an evening (please see page 256). When this occurs, the dry orgasm can feel very different from usual. Some men report that it has an unusual 'local' intensity – i.e., in the region of the penis.
- dry orgasms can also occur if the man has been taking certain prescription drugs, including some blood pressure pills. Clearly, if you suddenly have a dry climax, it's worth considering whether it's due to something which your doctor has put you on.
- some narcotic drugs can produce dry orgasms.
- if a male has trained himself in the curious Oriental technique of constricting the pelvic muscles just as orgasm begins, it's possible that no fluid will emerge.
- dry orgasms can also occur in early sexual life; quite frequently a boy may have attained the capacity to have climaxes, but has not yet started producing fluid. (Please see the next chapter, on how climaxes start in teenage years.)
- dry orgasms are also very nearly inevitable after most types of prostate surgery. Unfortunately, many patients are completely unaware that this is what will happen to them, and are pretty upset to find that they are no longer producing sex fluid.

So if you are considering undergoing a prostate operation, you should discuss this matter very carefully with your surgeon *before* going ahead. If you want to have further children, it may be advisable to make a pre-operative deposit of fluid in a sperm bank. Alternatively, it is sometimes possible to use special techniques in order to retrieve sperm from the man's body, even though he is not ejaculating them externally.

HOW LONG DO MALES TAKE TO REACH ORGASM?

One major difference between the sexes is the speed with which they can reach orgasm. Though there are a few women who can climax very fast from a 'standing start', this ability is rare. In contrast, the average male can come very quickly – far *too* quickly in many cases! Many women have complained bitterly to us about the rapidity with which their partners climax. A fairly typical comment is 'Three minutes and it's all over, and then he falls asleep.'

In fact, three minutes is quite long by some male standards. Dr Kinsey found clear evidence that there are pre-pubescent lads who actually reach a climax in ten seconds flat.

In teenage years, the male reaction time can be almost as fast as that. Forty years ago, one of us was an astonished spectator at dormitory 'orgasm races', in which the winning youths regularly achieved times of just under thirty seconds.

What about adulthood? Well, most fully grown males can actually climax in less time than it takes to boil an egg, *if they want to*. But as a chap grows more mature he usually slows up a bit – and also grasps the simple fact that women like men to 'last' a long time . . .

Nowadays, this vital tip has become much more widely known than it used to be. Back in Dr Kinsey's time, at the mid-point of the twentieth century, he was able to state with confidence that about three-quarters of all American males reached their climax within *two minutes* of starting intercourse!

Today, matters are very different. The male respondents to our survey claim, on average, that they make love to their partners for twenty-one minutes before ejaculating. Regrettably, we forgot to ask their female partners to confirm this optimistic view . . .

Still, it's good that things are improving and that men are trying to increase their 'staying power'. Shere Hite recently found that one-fifth of all American males would really like love-making to last more than an hour. A starry-eyed 7 per cent would like to keep it up for 'days, weeks or years'. For advice on how to last longer, see Chapter Fourteen.

HOW OFTEN DO MEN HAVE ORGASMS?

Unfortunately, men lie through their teeth about how often they have climaxes! So no one can say with any certainty what the average frequency is.

Even as this book went to press, a highly entertaining row was going on about a new survey which claims that French men have five times as many orgasms as Americans. And if you believe that, you'll believe anything. . .

We would urge you, dear reader, to look with considerable scepticism at any claim that the average male has *x* orgasms per week. Bear in mind that there are vast numbers of men who simply do not have any orgasms at all, perhaps because they are ill, or because a much-loved partner has died, or because they are now too old. Such people very rarely fill in sex surveys.

Having said all that, we now report to you that our 1995 sex survey has produced this result. *The average bloke who answered our questionnaire says he has FOUR orgasms per week.*

Actually, this is not an unreasonable figure – especially since we know that there are many males (particularly in their teens and twenties) who 'score' far more than this.

If the figure of four climaxes per week seems high to you, do keep in mind the fact that this means climaxes from *all* sources. In other words, the figure includes orgasms from masturbation, wet dreams, petting and so on, as well as orgasms from intercourse.

Indeed, we had one letter from a young man who summed things up very well when he wrote:

> I presume you mean *any* kind of orgasm. Last week I made love to my girlfriend three times, and had another climax when she touched me up in the car. I also had a wank when I woke up on Saturday morning, and I came in my sleep on Sunday night. Total: six.

There speaks a happy man . . .

Putting things in context, the new and highly authoritative American survey (published by the University of Chicago) finds that only 43 per cent of married males claim to have intercourse twice or more per week. The same survey shows that a quarter of single men have had no intercourse at all in the past year!

So you can see that there is tremendous individual variation – and therefore you should *not* feel bad if the number of climaxes which you yourself have is very different from the results that sex surveys throw up.

For instance, many years ago Dr Kinsey found that he had one perfectly healthy male 'subject' who had had just one orgasm in thirty years. In contrast, another 'subject' was a distinguished lawyer who had averaged over thirty orgasms per week over the previous three decades!

This extraordinary diversity in men's orgasmic needs is shown in Figure 11.7, which demonstrates very clearly that while most males seem to be very happy with between *one*

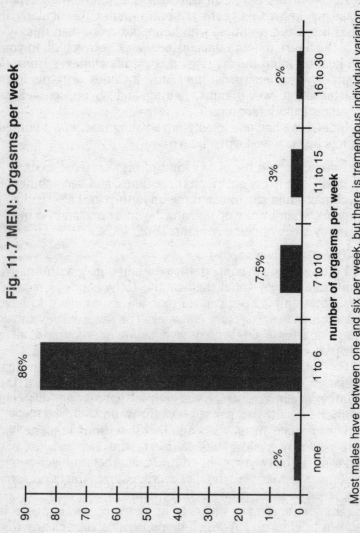

Fig. 11.7 MEN: Orgasms per week

Most males have between one and six per week, but there is tremendous individual variation

and six orgasms per week, a substantial minority have none at all – and another substantial minority have anything from seven to thirty. (Among this last group are some dihydro-testosterone-packed young fellows who will cheerfully tot up six in a single night – please see the section on multiple orgasms, toward the end of this chapter.)

One final point about frequency of orgasm: although we have already said that figures on this subject can never be very reliable, we do think that we have detected a curious trend in recent years.

It seems to us that people have started having more orgasms *since the world recession began*; certainly, our figures have gone up during this period.

Of course, the explanation may simply be that people have grown more sexually liberated in the 1990s, and that more sex is generally available. But it does seem perfectly reasonable that unemployed men and women might well start having more orgasms, merely because they have more time on their hands (if you'll forgive the phrase).

We also wonder whether unemployed people may have more time to fill in sex surveys . . .

HOW ORGASMS CHANGE THROUGH LIFE

Sadly, male orgasms do change a bit during life. And unlike women – whose climaxes tend to get better, easier, and more frequent – men do (quite frankly) find that they can't 'raise a canter' quite as often as they used to.

But here's the good news:

- the decline in frequency is *not* catastrophic; it is very much more gradual than most people imagine – as we'll see in a moment;
- as a chap gets older, he usually develops very much better *control* over his orgasms, which is one reason why many

men over forty do honestly believe that they are much better lovers than they were when they were seventeen or eighteen.

Our new survey – like all previous ones – does indeed show that frequency of orgasm does decline a little with age (see Figure 11.8).

But as you can see, there are large numbers of men in their forties, fifties, sixties and even beyond who are still happily having orgasms. Incidentally, a useful rule to remember is that at age seventy, 70 per cent of men are still potent!

If you're not terribly bothered about having orgasms, then of course it's perfectly OK to let your sexual activity 'wind down' as you get older (assuming your partner is also happy about this!).

But if you *are* keen on sex, and want to go on having orgasms until late in life, then the odds are that you will be able to do so. Our tips to you are:

• keep fit;
• don't smoke;
• don't drink too much;
• don't get overweight;
• have a partner who's enthusiastic about sex!

We have to rather reluctantly admit that the actual *nature* of orgasm changes a little as a man gets into the final decades of his life.

Masters and Johnson have detailed various ways in which they say that the climax in older males is different – though it must be said that their 'study population' in this age group was very small and, in our view, may not be typical of *all* ageing men.

Briefly, Masters and Johnson say that about the time a chap starts drawing his pension, he can expect that the time he takes to get an erection will be longer – but he will be able

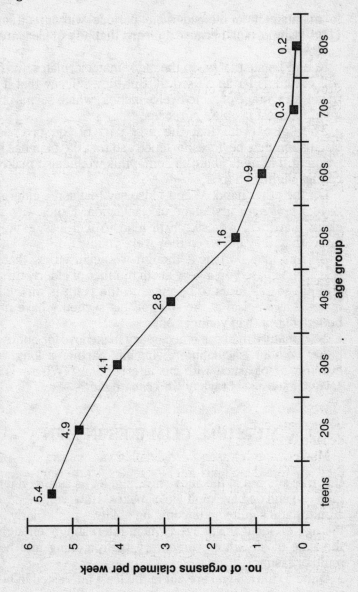

Fig. 11.8 MALES: number of orgasms claimed per week in various age groups

to maintain it for considerable periods without difficulty. (This is important, because it means that he can pleasure his partner.)

M and J state that when the older man ejaculates, his fluid will not go as far as it used to. But they still say that it will travel 'an average of six to twelve inches', which seems pretty good for most people's purposes!

They also claim that the first part of the process of ejaculation may be 'foreshortened', so that the man has little warning that he is about to come; this would also make his climax slightly shorter.

On the other hand, M and J also say that some older men have a *prolonged* first stage of ejaculation. Either way, they claim that men over sixty will tend to feel less 'expulsive force' than they did when they were younger.

All this may be true – though we again stress that the research is based on a very small number of elderly men.

What seems to us to be more to the point is this. Older males – as we said at the start of this section – have much better *control* than younger ones.

So, a mature man can if necessary make love for hours and hours without ejaculating, giving his partner a long, long evening of pleasure with no interruptions. Where is the seventeen-year-old toyboy who can do *that*?

MULTIPLE CLIMAXES IN MEN

If you're amazed at the above heading, let us assure you that men can and do have multiple climaxes! However, we have to admit that it's quite an uncommon ability – particularly over the age of about thirty-five (which, interestingly enough, is the time of life when women are really getting into being multi-orgasmic).

Quite frankly, if you are not in the least interested in being a multi-climax male, then we suggest you skip this section. Most blokes agree with the words of the old joke: 'Once a king, always a king; once a night . . . . is enough for anybody.'

What *is* a multiple climax? Basically the term implies that the man comes more than once in a sex session – say, in an evening. Quite a few guys can do this. But as we'll see in a moment, there are actually a few males who can do it again and again *during a single act of love-making*!

Yes, we know it sounds incredible. But scientific research has shown that there are men who can climax repeatedly in the way that women can. But let's look first at the more reasonable 'achievement' of orgasming more than once in an evening. The important thing to grasp is that this ability is age-related. In other words, it does get rather more difficult to do as you get older!

Figure 11.9 makes this clear. Based on the work of Kinsey, it shows that the younger you are, the more likely you are to have multiple orgasms. Round about the time of puberty, many boys who can have orgasms are capable of doing it again quite quickly – say, within half an hour.

In the mid-teenage years, some highly sexed young men are so multi-orgasmic that they can toss off – if you will forgive the expression – five or six climaxes in a night. (Incidentally, this is harmless – though it may leave them very tired next day, and possibly with a very puffy, swollen organ as well.)

By the age of twenty about one in six men is still multi-orgasmic. It is common for these lusty young fellows to turn this ability to their advantage in a curious way: before making love to a woman, they will have a 'preliminary' climax – which slows them down for the second one!

As one university student explained to us:

'I tend to be a bit too quick during intercourse. So half an hour before my fiancée pops round to see me, I have a climax by myself. Having done that, I can make love

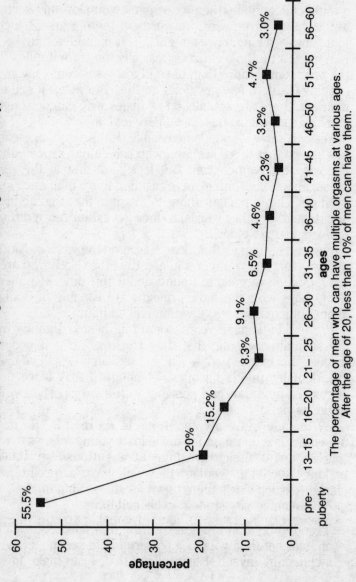

Fig. 11.9 MALES: Multiple orgasms at various ages (after Kinsey)

The percentage of men who can have multiple orgasms at various ages.
After the age of 20, less than 10% of men can have them.

to her for a couple of hours before I come again.'

This story points up an important fact about multiple climaxes in men: having the first one makes the second one slower – and so on.

Turning again to the question of age, you can see from figure 11.9 that by the age of thirty-five, only about 7 per cent of men seem to have the ability to 'do it' twice in an evening. And beyond fifty the ability is quite rare.

However, it can happen, provided the stimulus is sufficiently strong. We know of one case in which a fifty-something businessman went to Denmark with his wife on a package tour. Once in Copenhagen, both of them began to really *relax* (which was unusual for them). They also drank very little, and started feeling quite fit, and very romantic toward each other.

To their surprise, on the last night of their holiday the courier arranged a brief visit to an extremely sexy show. And when they returned to their bedroom, the couple found that the TV was showing a naked romp of the type which Scandinavian hotels seem to think is essential for their guests . . .

Not altogether surprisingly, the businessman made love to his delightful wife three times that night. And apparently she had a very nice time, too.

We're not sure that many men would actually *want* to have evenings like that, packed with multiple climaxes. But if you do, try the following:

- make sure that you and the woman you love are totally relaxed and happy together;
- try and be in reasonably fit condition;
- avoid heavy drinking (and heavy eating);
- set aside plenty of time for your love-making on the date in question – preferably at least four hours!
- if possible, ensure that you are away from home in a nice, romantic setting;

- use whatever aids that you think will turn both of you on;
- most important, do tell her what you're planning to do –
  and don't go ahead unless she agrees!

Up till now we've been talking about the fairly 'reasonable' target of just having more than one climax in a night. But what about these guys who are supposed to do it several times *during a single act of intercourse*?

Well, they do exist. Back in the 1960s, Masters and Johnson actually observed one man ejaculate three times in ten minutes in their lab! They sounded a bit surprised at this, but – like good scientists – merely confined themselves to reporting that 'the seminal fluid volume progressively was reduced in amount with each ejaculatory episode'.

Up until recently, some researchers had considerable trouble in believing this story. But Drs Marian Dunn and Jan Trost have now published a careful study of a group of American and Swedish men who regularly have several orgasms within a very short time, while having intercourse.

Amazingly, they ranged in age from twenty-five up to sixty-nine, and their average age was forty-three. Even more astonishingly, some of them have become multi-orgasmic in later life – learning to do it well after the age of thirty-five.

The men who have been multi-orgasmic all their lives reported that for many years they *did not think there was anything unusual about themselves*! Drs Trost and Dunn say in a medical journal: 'Most thought that *all* men were multiply orgasmic. Usually, it was a partner who first made them aware that they were unusual.'

What extraordinary conversations those must have been! ('Sven, darling: has anyone ever told you that you're a little different from other men in bed?')

What about the chaps who *learned* to be multiply orgasmic after the age of thirty-five? How on earth did they do it?

We regret to inform you that there is no magic secret. Most of them just seem to have developed the ability by chance, probably through continuing thrusting after they had finished the first orgasm inside their wives. (Drs Dunn and Trost report straight-faced that one middle-aged gent who found this happening to him promptly shouted 'DOUBLEE!' –which is apparently a shooting expression, used to indicate that you have hit two clay pigeons . . .)

However, some men actually did *make* themselves multi-orgasmic. They had read in women's magazines about females being multiply orgasmic, and they decided that they could do the same! They appear to have done this by using a mental technique in which the mind prevents the body from releasing part or all of its ejaculate at the moment of orgasm.

Curiously enough, we have been told of a closely related Tantric method by two therapists who practise oriental meditation in Forest Hill, London.

Similarly in 1995, Californian sex therapist and sexual surrogate Barbara Keesling published a book (*How To Make Love All Night: Male Multiple Orgasm and Other Secrets For Prolonged Lovemaking*, Little Brown Inc.) in which she says that by controlling his 'PC' muscle (see page 305), a man can learn to give himself multiple climaxes, by reaching orgasm without ejaculating. It's actually the one that makes your penis twitch upwards when you suddenly contract it. If you do this *now*, you'll realise that it's also the one that enables you to stop yourself peeing when you don't want to. Exercising it is said to be good for your sexual health. And Barbara Keesling – like some of the Tantric school – maintains that if you learn to twitch it midway through an orgasm, you can stop the fluid coming out – and so ensure that you'll have another one very soon. We most definitely do NOT guarantee this!

Whether you want to try and follow the example of the gallant Swedish and Californian masters of the multiple orgasm is up to you. For the record, most of them say that they have between *two and nine* orgasms per sex session. One chap in Sweden says he has had as many as sixteen in a single prolonged act of intercourse with a lady.

This must have been a trifle tiring, to say the very least.

FAKING MALE ORGASM

One of the more surprising findings of our survey has been the fact that so many men are *faking* it these days.

As we all know – especially if we've watched *When Harry Met Sally* – it is quite easy for women to 'fake it', and many ladies do. Our survey suggests that six out of ten women have gone through the bogus 'Shriek – Shriek – I'm coming – I'm coming' routine.

But *men*? Yes, it happens. According to our survey, about a quarter of males have faked a climax at some time!

You might think that this would be very difficult, since one can hardly fake an ejaculation. But if you think about it, there's usually such a lot of fluid sloshing about during intercourse that it's not difficult for a chap to give a few theatrical groans and thrusts and then declare 'That was marvellous, darling; we must do it again sometime . . .'

Why would they fake it? Well, for some time we have been hearing from youth organisations that these days there is extraordinary pressure on young men to *perform* – and that some poor chaps find it difficult to manage. It's easy to see that a male who thinks that women *expect* you to come (or else you're not a 'real man') might well find himself running out of steam – and decide that the best thing to do is to terminate matters by pretending that he's got there.

This may happen with older men, too – but it's noticeable in our survey results that it is youngsters who are most likely to report having faked.

All of this is a bit daft really, isn't it? Both males and females should realise these facts:

• men cannot always 'perform' on command;

- if a chap is tired out, he probably won't be able to go all the way;
- if that happens, it's no snub to his partner;
- you can have very good sex *without* male orgasm at the end of it – and there's a lot to be said for the old saying 'Half tonight – and half tomorrow night . . .'

12

FIRST ORGASM IN MALES

How Climaxes Start • Pre-Puberty Orgasms • Orgasms at Puberty: the 'Big Day' for the Teenage Male • The Fluid at First Orgasm • What To Do If the First Orgasm Doesn't Arrive • What Happens Next • Health Warning

HOW CLIMAXES START

Until very recent years, most people didn't want to admit that male climaxes *do* start – usually in a very dramatic way – in early teenage years.

In most Western countries, boys were told nothing about the sexual earthquake that was about to hit them! Indeed, if you search the newspapers and magazines of the 1950s and 1960s, you will find virtually no mention of male puberty – and absolutely no help for youngsters who were struggling to come to terms with its devastating effects.

Even in the 1970s, one of us (D.D.) found as a doctor-journalist that it was enormously difficult to get permission to discuss puberty – male or female – in print or on TV. In the 1980s, the medical journal where D.D. worked was still receiving letters from doctors who thought that young men needed no sexual outlet till they got married at around the age of twenty-five. *What* a help these physicians must have been to their teenage patients . . .

You may find this incredible, but far into the l990s both of us were still having serious censorship problems when we tried to mention masturbation. ('We don't want that kind of thing at breakfast-time / lunch-time / tea-time / supper-time / bed-time, thank you.')

But the plain fact is that young male teenagers do have orgasms. And when they start happening, they often do so with such insistence and frequency that the boy's whole life is disrupted.

He may be terrified about what's happening to him, especially if no one has explained it to him. He may well be filled with colossal guilt feelings, which all too frequently will leave him hung-up about sex in adult life.

And regrettably, he may become a prey to people who exploit his newfound capacity to have orgasms for their own purposes. Sad to say, we have seen a lot of men who were seduced, at or soon after puberty, by pederastic youth leaders or churchmen. Again and again, the boy's parents had thought that the pederast was the sort of respected figure who would 'teach our lad all about growing up'. We need hardly tell you that being abused by an adult at puberty is likely to have lifelong consequences.

So, parents and teachers have a great responsibility to tell boys that *climaxes are going to happen to them*. It's also worth stressing to youngsters that climaxes won't do them any harm! (We get a lot of letters – mainly from young men of Asian ancestry – asking us to confirm that wet dreams or masturbation will weaken the health, shorten the life, and damage the spine . . .)

When do these climaxes start happening? In most Western countries the average is about $13\frac{3}{4}$ years. But in some boys, puberty and its associated orgasms begin considerably earlier – and a few find that nothing happens till several years later.

Figure 12.1 makes this 'spread' clear. As you can see, the vast majority of young lads (90 per cent in fact) will have their first climax between the ages of eleven and fifteen.

In about 8 per cent of lads, it'll happen before the age of twelve (so, parents: do please warn your sons early!); and in a couple of per cent, it doesn't happen till after the seventeenth birthday.

PRE-PUBERTY ORGASMS

For scientific accuracy, we have to point out that some males do begin having orgasms long *before* puberty. Admittedly, they're only a tiny minority, but they exist. Our hesitancy about putting these statistics into print is due to the fact that we have absolutely no desire to appear to be encouraging childhood sex.

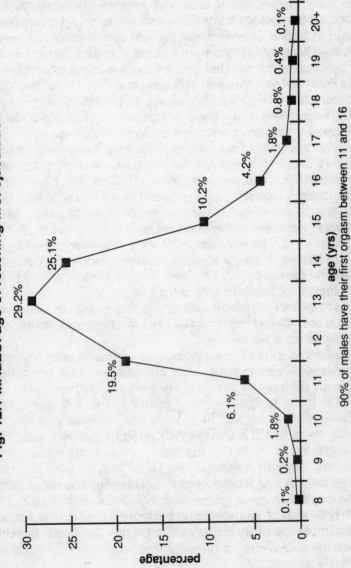

Fig. 12.1 MALES: age of reaching first ejaculation

90% of males have their first orgasm between 11 and 16

Nonetheless, the truth about pre-puberty orgasms has been in psychology textbooks for many years, and it isn't possible to deny it. If you've read the first half of this book, you'll know that our survey shows that some women report having climaxes long before puberty – and the same is true of men.

We're sorry if you find this shocking, but it's the way that nature has made a lot of humans. One cannot disagree with Dr Kinsey when he states: 'Orgasm has been observed in boys of every age, from five months to adolescence.'

Parents report that such orgasms are most often caused by rocking with the thighs together, or simply by self-masturbation. Almost incredibly in 1995 the Riverside Ferry Pre-Natal Clinic of Virginia claimed in a TV programme that they had clear ultra-sound evidence that the male *foetus* masturbates. We remain unconvinced . . .

Sadly, childhood climaxes may also be caused by interference from adult child-abusers. And some climaxes may be caused by sex play with other youngsters, especially in the years immediately before puberty.

Pre-puberty orgasms are 'dry' – that is, not accompanied by ejaculation. (Dry orgasms are discussed more fully in Chapter Fourteen.)

According to the textbooks, a curious feature of pre-puberty climaxes is that they are often multiple – in other words, the lad can do it again in a very short time.

Do these pre-pubescent orgasms do the boy any harm? Paediatricians say that they don't. A widespread view among experts is that if a child is noticed to be masturbating, the best thing to do is to simply distract him into some other activity, without making a fuss about it. (Don't tell him that 'It's awfully bad for his eyes . . .' This time-honoured myth just isn't true.)

Having said all this, it's important to realise that for the vast majority of males, orgasms do not start until puberty arrives.

ORGASMS AT PUBERTY: THE 'BIG DAY' FOR THE TEENAGE MALE

If you're a parent, it's a good idea to bear in mind that the day your son's first orgasm arrives is going to be one of the most significant of his whole life.

He may be frightened, ecstatic, bewildered, proud, guilty – or all five. Pleasant as an orgasm may be, it's quite an alarming experience if you don't understand the changes which are taking place in your own body. Of course, other boys may have told the lad what to expect. But ideally, his parents and/or teachers will have had the sense to explain to him about climaxes! At least, we hope so.

How do these first orgasms happen? In all sorts of ways – for instance, Salvador Dali had his first one by accident when he was shinning up a pine tree in Spain. (He later claimed to have fallen in love with the pine tree.)

Less surrealistically, have a look at Figure 12.2 which shows the various causes of first climax in males. It's based on the work of Dr Kinsey, done a long time ago. To the best of our knowledge, no one has ever successfully updated his research on this topic. Regrettably, though, when we asked *women* about the source of their first orgasm – see Chapter Three – we forgot to ask the men.

As you can see, the vast majority of first climaxes – about two-thirds, in fact – occur because the boy masturbates. Masturbation is a very natural act, particularly at that age. You can hardly expect a young chap whose body is crying out for release to ignore the fairly obvious proximity of his right hand to his insistent erection.

How do teenagers learn that orgasmic relief is possible through masturbation? It varies from culture to culture, but Shere Hite says that 60 per cent of American males simply found out by accident; 34 per cent had learned from a friend, and 4 per cent from books. Two per cent claimed to have

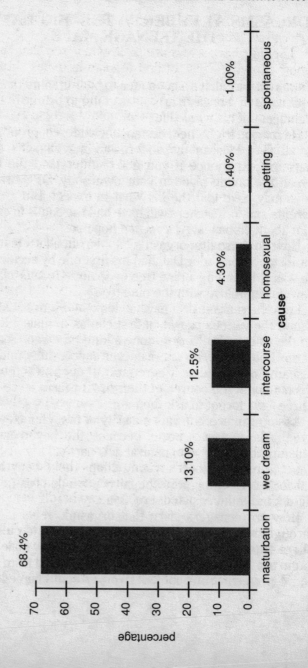

Fig. 12.2 MALES: cause of first-ever orgasm (after Kinsey)

learned 'from films' – though quite which films those were, we cannot imagine.

Looking back at Figure 12.2, you'll see that the second most common cause of first orgasm in males is the famous '*wet dream*' – which seems to account for about one in eight of all first climaxes. We dealt fully with wet dreams in Chapter Eleven; the important point to grasp about them is that males can't prevent themselves from having these dreams, so no matter how strictly a teenager has been brought up in regard to sexual matters, there's a very high chance that he will have these 'nocturnal emissions'.

So clearly, he should be warned that he's probably going to get them. Many young men have a frightful time trying furtively to clear up the semen stains caused by the dreams – stains which are often very big and very hard to hide at this age!

We know of one teenager who wears two pairs of swimming trunks under his pyjamas, with a handkerchief jammed in between, 'so that the spunk won't get on the sheets where Mum and Dad will see it.'

Yet the poor boy produces so much fluid in each dream that it *still* gets through and stains the bed-linen.

How much better it would be if teenagers and parents could communicate about these matters . . .

Returning to Figure 12.2, we can see the other possible causes of a male's first orgasm. Regrettably – or at least, it's regrettable in our view – some boys do achieve their first climax through having *sexual intercourse*.

One reason why it's regrettable is that our survey shows that these early teenage attempts at coitus are often completely unprotected – so they can hardly be described as 'safe sex'.

A smaller proportion of young males have their first orgasm through *homosexual activity*, as you can see. Most commonly, this is with lads of a similar age.

The authoritative British Wellcome survey has recently

confirmed that men who have been to boarding schools are
much more likely to have had early homosexual experiences
of this sort. Parents who are thinking of sending their sons
to that type of school may care to reflect that mutual
masturbation in the 'dorm' might well prove to be their
offspring's first experience of orgasm . . .

What other sources of first climax are there? As you'll
observe from the illustration, Kinsey recorded that about
one in 100 males had his first climax *'spontaneously'*. This is
not just fantasy: we saw in the previous chapter that
spontaneous orgasms definitely do happen in males! In
addition, a very small number of teenagers manage to bring
themselves to climax just by thinking sexy thoughts.

Back at the mid-twentieth century, Dr Kinsey also found
that one in 300 men said that they had their first 'Big O'
through *petting*. Although we have no statistics ourselves, we
venture to suggest that the figure might be considerably
higher in most Western countries today, since our
researches show that very large numbers of teenagers now
go in for hand-petting, or even mouth-petting – with partners
of the opposite sex. (Most of our female respondents said
that they started some sort of petting at around the age of
fourteen.)

Frankly, we are *not* too wild about this epidemic of petting
in such very young people – but we do think that at least it's
preferable to full intercourse.

THE FLUID AT FIRST ORGASM

Now, one little-known fact about first orgasms at puberty:
they are often 'dry' – in other words no fluid is produced.
This may be a considerable worry to the teenager, especially
if he has been told by his friends that climaxes produce
'spunk'. But in fact, the lack of fluid is just a reflection of the

relative immaturity of his sexual equipment, and fluid will actually be produced within a few weeks or months (see also page 248).

When the liquid is first produced it may be *clear* or *greyish* – and this too may be a source of alarm to the young man if he has been informed that 'men squirt out *white* stuff'. But in fact, the fluid will take on the normal adult milky appearance before long.

As far as is known by medical science, these early ejaculations do usually contain sperms. So it's most important that young male teenagers should be under no illusions about the fact that *they are capable of getting girls pregnant*. Sadly, a lot of boys have the potentially disastrous idea that they are 'too young to father a child'.

WHAT TO DO IF THE FIRST ORGASM DOESN'T ARRIVE

Males are always worrying that there's something wrong with their sex organs, and male teenagers are no exception! Quite understandably, if a boy is told by all his classmates that *they* are having orgasms, and he *isn't*, then he may well become pretty anxious. Similarly, parents are likely to be concerned if they become aware that their son doesn't seem to have reached puberty at the same time as his friends.

Best thing to do in these circumstances is to have a look back at Figure 12.1. As it shows, 90 per cent of young men will become orgasmic between eleven and fifteen. In only about 2 per cent is it delayed beyond the seventeenth birthday.

Our medical advice is that until a teenager is approaching about fifteen and a half, there is nothing to worry about. But if at that stage he is showing no signs of puberty (which means not just orgasms, but also body, facial and pubic hair, and also increase in height and muscularity), then he should be checked out by his family doctor. It may be necessary to send him to an endocrinologist for some hormone tests.

This book is intended for *adults*. But if by any chance you are a young teenager who has dipped into it, and you're reading this section because you're concerned about your development, our advice to you is simply 'Don't worry!' Nearly *all* males do eventually achieve full sexual maturity and go on to have normal sex lives and (if they wish) become fathers.

If you need further advice or counselling, it's a good idea to contact one of the many Youth Advisory Clinics which have sprung up in recent times, such as the Brook Advisory Centres in Britain, or Family Service Youth Clinics in America, or Family Planning Federation Clinics in Australia. Student health schemes (where they are available) are also very good for providing confidential and reassuring advice.

WHAT HAPPENS NEXT

What happens next? The important thing to remember about male teenage orgasm is this. Once a young man starts having climaxes, he is usually going to carry on having them for the rest of his life (health permitting!).

Females are quite different in this respect. Our findings are that many young women will have their first orgasm through discovering masturbation, and will be quite intrigued by it – but a lot of them will simply not bother to do it again, and may have no further orgasm for months or even years.

In stark contrast, the dihydrotestosterone-driven male will usually feel compelled to have regular climaxes from the beginning onwards – which means right through the ages

14, 15, 16, 17 and so on. To paraphrase Oscar Wilde, having a first orgasm is likely to be the start of a lifelong love affair with one's penis.

For most males that's the way it is. As Dr Kinsey says:

'After the initial experience in ejaculation, practically all males become regular in their sexual activity . . . The male, in the course of his life, may change the sources of his sexual outlet, and his frequencies may vary through the weeks and months, and over a span of years, but almost never is there a complete cessation of his activity until such time as old age finally stops all response.'

HEALTH WARNING

Once again, we stress that this book is intended for adults, but if you happen to be a male teenager who's decided to have a peep at it, could we just remind you of the following:

- at your age, you are highly fertile – so if you have an orgasm inside a girl, there is a considerable risk that you will get her pregnant;
- orgasms *outside* her body could also be risky, if your sperm gets carried (say, on your hands) to her vagina – but the danger is much less;
- the world is full of STDs (Sexually Transmitted Diseases) and in some parts of it, there is a considerable risk of AIDS;
- for everybody's sake, try and practise safe sex;
- if you're desperate for an orgasm, petting or (better still) masturbation are far safer than intercourse!

13

MEN'S VIEWS ABOUT ORGASM

Men Look at it In a *very* Different Way From Women • The
Importance of Evolution • The Male Obsession With
Penetration • Men's Views on Oral Sex • Do They Think
that Orgasm is Necessary? • How Does Orgasm *feel* to
Them? • What Do They Think About *your* Orgasms?

MEN LOOK AT IT IN A VERY DIFFERENT WAY FROM WOMEN!

A vital thing for any woman reading this book to grasp is this: **men do not look at orgasms in the same way as women do!**

As we've shown in our survey, very few females regard orgasm as essential to life. A lot of women enjoy it tremendously, and experience great heights of pleasure when they come, but most of them say that if climaxes were removed from their lives, it wouldn't be the end of the world . . .

In contrast, what does the average male think? He would be *desolate* without orgasms. Indeed, we have had many thousands of letters from elderly men who have more or less reached the end of their sexual lives, and who are absolutely distraught that they can no longer climax. (N.B. Some of them can be helped – so it's always worth consulting a doctor.)

The male 'addiction' to orgasms is so powerful that younger men – who are, of course, the most orgasmic – will quite frequently cajole their unwilling girlfriends with the old chatline of 'If I don't have a climax, I'll get *ill*.'

Is this actually true? No. But it is a fact that if a man is deprived of his regular climaxes, he will very often get a rather wearing pain in his testicles. This is known rather light-heartedly to doctors as *orchitis amorosa acuta*. In America, they call it 'lover's nuts . . .'

The pain is much more likely to happen if a young chap has become sexually excited by a girl, or if she has given him a lot of sexual stimulation, but stopped short of giving him an orgasm. This is often called 'the Prick-Tease Syndrome'.

Incidentally, women should not let themselves be blackmailed by blokes in this way. If a man is getting testicular pain because he hasn't climaxed, then the remedy is in his own hands . . .

Women readers should be quite clear about men's orgasmic drive: many males – particularly those dihydro-testosterone drenched younger ones – would do almost ANYTHING for an orgasm, and particularly one that involves a pretty woman.

They will lie to women ('Don't worry, darling: I'm sterile'); they will cheat their own best friends ('*Certainly* I'll take Jennifer home for you, Bill'); they will sometimes offer outrageous sums of money ('Would a thousand dollars change your mind, my darling?'). And all of this is in the quest for just a few seconds of pleasure – admittedly, pretty exquisite pleasure.

It's no surprise, is it, that Kinsey was able to find a chap who had gone through the whole of his adult life having thirty orgasms a week!

On a slightly less dramatic scale, Kerry – a twenty-five-year-old Australian journalist – told us that he felt his life had been 'dominated' by the search for orgasms since he was fourteen.

'I keep a diary, and mark them in it,' he said. 'And I have to admit, I get pretty worried if my score starts dropping. If it's not above twenty a month, I get to thinking that maybe I'm over the hill, or losing my virility.'

Over a pint of beer, Kerry explained to us that his principal concern was the fact that although he had been able to manage up to five climaxes a night as a young teenager, he was now down to two – 'or maybe three, if the Sheila's very exciting.'

We tried to convince him that he is in fact extremely virile for his age. But we were not altogether successful.

THE IMPORTANCE OF EVOLUTION

Why are so many men (admittedly, not all) so wild about orgasms?

The answer lies in the history of the human race. If you go back a million years or so, the primitive man who was most likely to have children *was the guy who desperately wanted climaxes*. Males who *didn't* want orgasms weren't very likely to have offspring!

The characteristics of parents do tend to be passed on, so the men who wanted the most orgasms tended to populate the world with sons who wanted a lot of orgasms, too. And this has gone on for thousands of generations, with males who needed a lot of climaxes always 'out-breeding' the ones who didn't.

So when you think about it, it's rather surprising that there are so many blokes around who *don't* spend their lives wondering where the next orgasm is coming from.

THE MALE OBSESSION WITH PENETRATION

If you're a woman, we'd like you to appreciate the fact that men don't just want to have climaxes – they want to have them *inside you*!

The average male tends to rate his orgasms on a 'scale of desirability', which is something like this:

TYPE OF CLIMAX:	RATING:
IN HIS SLEEP	OK
MASTURBATION	NICE
BEING FRIGGED BY YOU	GREAT!
IN YOUR MOUTH	WONDERFUL!
IN YOUR VAGINA	GLORIOUS! THE VERY BEST

These 'ratings' are completely understood by all reasonably highly sexed young males. If you could overhear their boyish conversations, we're afraid that they'd go something like this:

'How did you get on last night, then?'
'Oh . . . only to First Base. You know – just a hand job.'
'Tough. Mine . . . well, I shouldn't tell you this really – but she went down on me. It was fantastic . . .'
'You lucky guy! Still, I'm seeing Sandra on Saturday. And she *goes all the way*.'

So there you have it. To a male who is desperate for sex, any orgasm with you (in your hand, over your thighs, over your breasts – *especially* over your breasts) is very good, but doing it after *penetrating* you in some way is much, much better. Sorry, dear female readers – but that's how they are.

So the male desire for penetration of the female – once again, influenced by 30,000 generations of evolution – is colossally strong. It's noticeable from the intimate conversation of younger men that the *depth* of this penetration is of tremendous importance to them. One hears phrases like:

'I got it really *deep* into her . . .'
'It was as far in as I could get it . . .'
'And then I pushed it in even more . . .'

This desire to thrust deeply does, we are afraid to say, apply to all of your available orifices. Virtually every heterosexual male wants to get into the vagina as far as possible. Quite a substantial minority are ecstatic about the idea of thrusting deep into the female bottom, though this is *not* something we are recommending in this era of AIDS!

And then, of course, there is your mouth . . .

MEN'S VIEWS ON ORAL SEX

Now – what about male orgasm in the female mouth?

Once again, we must apologise if the subject appals you, but facts must be faced. We've already seen that these days the majority of men are keen on oral sex. In the 1995 University of Chicago study of American males, no less than 27 per cent said that they'd actually had it *in their most recent sexual encounter*. Similarly, the massive Wellcome study has found that 69 per cent (!) of British males had had fellatio from a woman.

We have to report that most men who have enjoyed fellatio think that the ideal conclusion of it is reaching orgasm inside the lady's mouth. In the recent *New Woman/Arena* magazine survey, 55 per cent of males said that this was what they wanted – and furthermore, they thought that the partner should swallow the 'come'. Harry, a young American law student, told us:

> 'I think that this is the most intimate and loving thing that a woman can do for a man. I lived for a long time with another law student – a feminist – and although she was real keen on sex, swallowing sperm was the one thing she would not do for me. She thought it degraded females.
>
> 'Eventually, I fell in love with an older woman, who is now my partner. Several times a month she will go down on me, and carry on giving me head until I climax. Then she seems to take great, great pleasure in swallowing what I've produced. To me, that implies total, total acceptance.'

Well, while many women are perfectly happy with the kind of 'totally accepting' activity that Harry describes, a lot of females find it quite disgusting! We cannot stress strongly enough that no-one should be pressured into doing this kind of thing against her will.

However, the prevalence of this male desire to come over somebody's tonsils does reinforce what we've already said: that men are 'programmed' to want to reach orgasm *inside* the female body.

Furthermore, their enthusiasm for deep penetration does, unfortunately perhaps, extend to oral sex as well as to the vaginal variety. Male erotic fiction is heavily laced with the image of the 'virile' guy who gets as far down his girlfriend's throat as possible when he climaxes.

Yet in practice, this is a less than brilliant idea, for the simple reason that all human beings have something called a 'gag reflex', which makes them try to throw up if something is pushed deep into the throat.

Some very experienced women have trained themselves to 'abolish' this gag reflex, and the same is true of a lot of gay men. It was the ability not to gag which led to the worldwide (if brief) fame of Miss Linda Lovelace, the star of the movie *Deep Throat*.

Frankly, we would suggest to male readers of this book that they should *not* pressurise their partners into deep oral penetration as climax approaches – since this can easily cause distress. It is perfectly possible to orgasm through fellatio *without* making the poor woman feel sick .

DO THEY THINK THAT ORGASM IS NECESSARY?

So we've seen that most men – though not all – are pretty obsessed with their own orgasms. But do they actually think that it's *vital* to reach an orgasm every time they have sex?

We are relieved to report that recent research appears to show that quite a lot of them may have grasped the simple fact that you can have rewarding, loving sex without actually coming. Yes, the British Wellcome study has found that just over a third of male Brits now disagree with the notion that 'Sex without orgasm cannot be really satisfying for a man'.

We find that this 'gentler' view of sex is commoner as men get older – perhaps for the fairly obvious reason that males do have less climaxes as the years go by. Many middle-aged and elderly males are quite content to make love to their partners for an hour or two *without* reaching orgasm. Indeed, a recent survey by a male magazine found that only 58 per cent of men 'always' ejaculate during sex. However, another 35 per cent nearly always do . . .

HOW DOES ORGASM FEEL TO THEM?

If you're a woman, you may well wonder how orgasm feels to men. It feels very nice indeed! Quite apart from all the romance, eroticism and (we hope) love that is so often associated with it, the fact remains that the simple experience of pumping out that ejaculate offers a male the most pleasurable physical experience he will have in his entire life.

In particular, men tend to derive enormous pleasure from two things:

- the feeling when the fluid rushes into the pipe at the base of the penis and forcefully expands it (see Figure 11.3, page 226);
- the intensely agreeable sensation as the fluid pumps out of the penis (and, very often, into *you*).

However, it's very difficult to put into words just *exactly* what a male feels during a climax. Heaven knows, enough poets and novelists have tried it – and frequently failed.

But we did ask several large groups of men to describe their sensations to us, using their own words. If you're a

cynical or sophisticated type of person, you may well be
inclined to sneer at these fairly simple phrases. All we can
say is: *you try and do better*!

Men's descriptions of their own orgasms

This is what they told us male orgasm was like:

- 'like a bullet from a gun – a huge relief.'
- 'like a volcano exploding in my penis.'
- 'all my insides being pulled out through my penis with
  little quakes.'
- 'like a rocket taking off and exploding in the sky.'
- 'like an angel crying on my tongue – and just for a second,
  I know how to fly.'
- 'like a flock of sparrows under my foreskin.'
- 'like scoring a winning touchdown.'
- 'a sudden rush of power and release from my penis.'
- 'like the apple blossom of my life – it's heaven.'

WHAT DO THEY THINK ABOUT YOUR ORGASMS?

What do men think about *female* orgasms? We find that men
are, in general, still a bit vague about female climaxes and
how they are caused – but they're learning!

A lot still have the mistaken idea that sexual intercourse
alone – no matter how brief – should be enough to bring a
woman off. ('If she doesn't come, she's probably a lesbian . . .')

A few are still daft enough to believe that they don't have
to touch the clitoris to make a female have a climax. ('That
little button doesn't do anything for *me*, thank you.')

According to the Wellcome survey, 37 per cent think that
sex without orgasm 'can't be really satisfying for a woman' –
this is appreciably higher than the percentage of women who

think the same thing.

The average guy probably doesn't know that his partner sometimes masturbates to orgasm – we found that only 49 per cent of men know this. But if he knew, he almost certainly wouldn't mind; 98 per cent of males said this, and 77 per cent were turned on by the idea . . .

14

WHEN MALE ORGASM GOES WRONG

It's a Delicate Mechanism • Coming a Bit Too Soon • Premature Ejaculation • Not Being Able to Come ('Ejaculatory Incompetence') • Dry Orgasms • Inability to Ejaculate May Not Necessarily Mean You Can't Have Children

ITS A DELICATE MECHANISM

Orgasm is a very complicated business – much more complicated than people think. No car designer or computer manufacturer could possibly invent a mechanism of the sheer complexity of the one that controls human orgasm.

A climax involves a quite extraordinary cooperation between the brain, the spinal cord, a large number of nerves, and a lot of tiny blood vessels. It involves the discharge of all sorts of body chemicals – some of which doctors are only just beginning to learn about.

So it's hardly surprising that the slightest little thing can very easily interfere with the process of climax – making it too quick, or too slow or preventing it from happening at all.

In this chapter, we'll look at what can go wrong with a male climax – and how to put matters right.

COMING A BIT TOO SOON

'Coming a bit too soon' is far and away the most widespread difficulty that men have in bed.

If you've read the results of our survey way back at the beginning of this book – you'll know that we found that no less than *six out of ten* males said that they sometimes come too soon. (This is in addition to the 10 per cent of males who *always* come too soon; see page 15.)

This finding confirms what sex experts have said for years: that millions of chaps all over the world can't quite control their climaxes, and often find themselves firing off before they mean to!

Not only does this cause some dissatisfaction for the man; it can – and frequently does – cause considerable frustration for the woman. Again and again, our female respondents have told us 'He comes too soon for me' or 'I only wish he could keep it up for three times as long'.

So what's to be done about it? Well, we think that every man should read our suggestions for *slowing down*.

Here they are:

- before you start on a sex session with your partner, try and have a clear image in your mind of *how long you want it to go on for* (twenty minutes? thirty minutes? forty minutes?);
- at all costs, make sure that you've talked the matter over with her *beforehand* – so that she knows that you're trying to prolong matters, and can help you;
- agree with her that you'll spend plenty of time on love-play before you start intercourse;
- during all this love play, do *tell* her if you feel you're 'getting near' so that she'll know that she must stop stimulating you for a bit;
- when you actually start having sexual intercourse, *both* of you must take it easy for a while; it's important that she shouldn't thrust a lot (or squeeze you with her pelvic floor [PC] muscles!) at moments when you're feeling pretty hyped up;
- similarly, ask her not to say rude or erotic things to you when you're obviously getting to a high point of raunchiness;
- during intercourse, concentrate on making *gentle slow* thrusts – and *withdraw* from her body frequently if you think things are getting too exciting;
- if you're getting too 'souped up', think very hard about other (and very boring) things, like the price of cod;
- if you're desperate, biting the pillow sometimes helps!

Good luck – and remember one cheering thought: as you grow older, you *will* develop better control . . .

PREMATURE EJACULATION

Up till now, we've been talking about a relatively trivial matter: coming a little bit too soon sometimes. But what if you've got more serious problems? What if you *always* come too soon – like about 10 per cent of men in our survey? Well, in that case, we think it best that you get professional help, from a doctor or from a clinic specialising in sexual matters. What are the treatments which are used for premature ejaculation (often known as 'hair-trigger trouble' because the poor man goes off too soon, like an easily-fired gun)?

These are the main ones at the moment:

- applying local anaesthetic ointment to the penis, in order to try and numb the sensations which he receives. Frankly, we do *not* recommend this method.

  Why? Well firstly, it doesn't really work. Secondly, the local anaesthetic will obviously get on to the woman's delicate bits as well as the man's. Thirdly, local anaesthetics can sometime cause a really *painful* 'sensitivity reaction'.

- prescription drugs. Frankly, these are not awfully effective at the moment. Some doctors prescribe anti-depressant pills, and a few give tranquillisers. Certainly, the *sedation* produced by a tranquilliser will sometimes take the edge off a guy's over-excitability – in the same way that a stiff drink can.

  But you have to remember that tranquillising drugs have side-effects and are addictive. So until somebody invents some totally new medication which delays climax time, we will not be recommending drug treatment.

- Masters-Johnson ('Squeeze') therapy. This gives great results. The couple – *not* just the man – really need to learn it carefully from a trained therapist. But if you want to attempt some do-it-yourself treatment, we'll give you the basics of the method here.

Briefly, it depends on the discovery that a particular way of squeezing the penis will 'turn off' the desire to come – just like pressing a finger on your upper lip turns off the desire to sneeze.

The famous squeeze does *not* hurt at all, so don't be fearful! It's shown in Figure 14.1.

Proceed as follows:

• make sure that both you and your partner are agreed that you're going to work together to beat this condition. Trying it *without* telling her what's going on is most unlikely to work. Allow at least an hour for every 'training session'.

• at your first training session, both of you should be naked. You lie flat on your back on the bed, and she kneels or sits facing you.

• ask her to 'rub up' your cock in the usual way – that is, start giving you a hand-job.

• When ever you start feeling the urge to come, tell her *at once*.

• she should immediately stop rubbing, and apply the squeeze grip, as shown in Figure 14.1. This will instantly stop you from wanting to climax.

• once the desire to orgasm has gone, ask her to start rubbing again.

• continue in this fashion for an hour or so. You can have a climax at the end if you want to, and so of course can she. *But do not attempt sexual intercourse.*

• after several weeks of this training you should be feeling *much* more confident about your ability to control yourself.

• then – and only then – can the two of you start to experiment with making a start on sexual intercourse.

• you need to do it in this way! During a training session, she should move gently forward till she is *kneeling astride you*. When you're feeling thoroughly under control, she should just put the tip of your penis inside her, and let you thrust a bit.

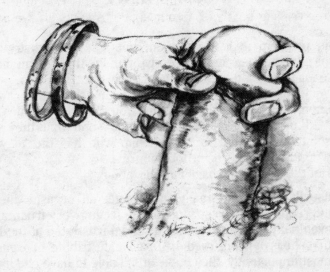

Fig. 14.1

Whenever you feel any urge to climax, she must 'withdraw', and immediately apply the squeeze grip.

- you'll probably have to continue with the routine described for several more weeks before you feel assured enough to go ahead with ordinary sexual intercourse.

  Good luck!

The above scheme may seem a bit wacky, but Masters and Johnson cured 98 per cent of their premature ejaculators with it. And we have talked to literally hundreds of men who have been turned from 'one-minute wonders' into 'half-hour heroes'.

Nonetheless, we do stress that by far the best results are obtained if the two of you work *with a therapist*.

NOT BEING ABLE TO COME ('EJACULATORY INCOMPETENCE')

This problem is less common, but it's very frustrating. Typically, the man finds out early on in life that he can make love for hours and hours – but scarcely ever climaxes.

Very often, this makes him enormously popular with women, once the word gets round! You see, a lot of ladies are so fed up with guys who come too soon that they are absolutely delighted to find a chap who has the 'staying power' to last for three or four hours . . .

But there are drawbacks to this 'ability':

- usually, the man simply cannot get an orgasm during intercourse, and so spends his life feeling very frustrated;
- eventually, his partner may also feel frustrated at the fact that she is never offered the usual male 'tribute' of orgasm;
- most importantly, the couple aren't able to have children.

So what can be done about this condition?

The most effective treatment available at the moment is the one developed by experts such as Dr Helen Singer Kaplan, of Cornell University. Basically, the idea is to help the man get rid of inhibitions about ejaculating inside the vagina. This involves the following steps:

- the couple are fully counselled;
- they are encouraged to go in for whatever form of sexual activity WILL give the man an orgasm – for instance, being 'frigged' by hand by his partner (even if this takes two hours or so);
- over a period of weeks or months, the couple continue these 'hand-job' sessions, but are taught how to bring the man's orgasm nearer and nearer to the woman's vaginal opening;
- eventually they reach a stage where the wife can put the

husband's penis inside her *just before he comes*;

• having achieved one orgasm inside her vagina, he gradually learns over a period of time to achieve it as a result of intercourse alone – rather than as the end-point of a hand-job.

As you'll appreciate, this programme is not an easy one to follow – and it would be very unwise to try and 'treat yourself' along these lines. It's far better to go to a sexual medicine clinic and be guided by them.

DRY ORGASMS

Men sometimes find that no fluid comes out when they climax; this is called a 'dry orgasm'. Quite often this is nothing to worry about; for instance, if you've already climaxed several times that day, you may simply have run out of spunk!

But dry climaxes can have more significant causes, such as damage caused by prostate surgery. You'll find a list of possible causes in Chapter Eleven (see page 248).

Even if you *always* have dry orgasms, it may be possible for you to become a parent – please see the next section.

INABILITY TO EJACULATE MAY NOT NECESSARILY MEAN YOU CAN'T HAVE CHILDREN

If you're unlucky enough to have dry orgasms – or even if you never climax at all – there is a chance that, thanks to modern medical techniques, you may be able to father children. So it's definitely worth consulting a fertility clinic to see if they can help you.

For instance, if you have dry climaxes as a result of prostate surgery, what's actually happening as a rule is that your sperm are going *into your bladder* instead of squirting out of your penis.

But it's possible for a fertility specialist to collect the sperms from your urine – and to use them to 'inseminate' your partner *via* her vagina.

Similarly, in some cases of male infertility caused by blockage of the 'plumbing', it's now possible to put a fine needle into the testicle and tap off some sperms. It may then be necessary to use microscopic techniques to inject a sperm directly into the partner's egg (ovum) – a method which was only developed in the 1990s.

Finally, if you cannot climax because of a severe spinal injury, it may still be possible to help you to father children. Using a method pioneered at the world-famous Bourn Hall Clinic in England, doctors can now pass an electric current through the region of a paraplegic man's prostate gland and so cause an ejaculation. They can then collect the sperm, and use it to fertilise his wife.

15

HOW TO HAVE A BETTER ORGASM – A GUIDE FOR MEN

Why Do You Want To Have Better Orgasms?
Step One: Get Yourself a Loving Partner
Step Two: Get Yourself Sexually Fit
Step Three: Make Sure It's *safe* Sex
Step Four: Get the Setting Right
Step Five: Teach Your Partner What You Want
Step Six: Slow Things up for a Better Climax
Step Seven: Use Fantasy Together
Step Eight: Make Special Occasions Together
Step Nine: Make *her* Happy Too

WHY DO YOU WANT TO HAVE BETTER ORGASMS?

Before you start out on this step-by-step guide to better male orgasms, can we just ask you one thing?

Why do you want better orgasms? If your climaxes are perfectly OK at the moment, then there's not really a lot of point in reading this chapter. You'd probably do better to turn to Chapter Ten – which will give you advice on how to make your PARTNER'S orgasms nicer!

But if you really are keen to get yourself better climaxes – and perhaps more of them – then please read on . . .

STEP ONE: GET YOURSELF A LOVING PARTNER

This is the first step – and perhaps the most vital one – in ensuring that you have good orgasms.

Frankly, you are *not* going to have the world's greatest orgasms on your own, are you? Climaxes from masturbation can be very intense, but they don't measure up to climaxes in the arms of a desirable woman. And it shouldn't just be *any* old desirable woman, either! Sure, you can have quite powerful orgasms with a 'professional' lady, or with someone you pick up on a one-night stand.

But all our research indicates that a really happy love-life – with lots of nice orgasms – is only likely to happen with a female partner who you're really used to – and who is used to you!

To be honest, it's best if you love her, and she loves you. If you aren't already in this enviable situation, then we wish you good luck in the search for the woman of your dreams . . .

STEP TWO: GET YOURSELF SEXUALLY FIT

One of us (D.D.) has seen a long succession of men who
were unhappy with their sex lives. Many – though not all – of
these chaps were:

• unfit;
• badly overweight;
• heavy drinkers;
• heavy smokers.

It is extremely difficult to be sexually fit and have really
good orgasms if you are in any of the above four categories.
So let's see how *you* can get yourself in tip-top shape for
climaxes:

General muscular fitness – including the sex muscle

If you want to have a good and highly orgasmic sex life, we
strongly recommend that you take some regular physical
exercise.

Running or swimming three times a week will help
considerably, and it need only be for twenty to twenty-five
minutes per session. Working out in a gym is also useful,
especially if you do exercises to build up the stomach
muscles and prevent yourself from having a saggy belly (see
next section).

What about exercising your *sex* muscle? Well, your sex
muscle isn't what many people think: there are *no* muscles
inside your penis!

However, there *is* a sex muscle in the lower part of your
body, and many men claim that if you exercise it regularly,
you will improve your sexual performance, and your
orgasms.

Indeed, there have actually been claims that regular
exercise of this 'love muscle' can help a chap achieve the

famous 'multiple orgasms' (see Chapter Eleven).

For instance in 1995, famed American sex therapist and *Playboy* centrefold Barbara Keesling published a startling book in which she claimed that building up this muscle will give a man such stamina that he can go on making love for many hours, having climax after climax. The book is called *How To Make Love All Night: Male Multiple Orgasm and Other Secrets for Prolonged Lovemaking* (published by Little, Brown, Inc.) and it maintains that once you have developed your 'love muscle', you can have orgasm after orgasm *without ejaculation.* (This echoes the views of some Eastern Tantric philosophers – please see the section on multiple orgasm in Chapter Eleven.)

Whether these entertaining claims are true or not, we think you *can* benefit from regular exercise of this sex muscle, which is really called the 'PC muscle'.

Here's how to do it:

- first identify your PC muscle. Do this by pretending that you're trying very hard to stop yourself from passing urine.
- if you're doing it right, this 'twitch' should make your penis and balls ride suddenly upwards. If you're in doubt whether this is happening, do the twitch in front of a mirror.
- repeat the twitch twenty times – then, after a few seconds' relaxation, do it another twenty times.
- go through the whole routine every morning and evening for at least six months, by which time your PC muscle should be really well developed.
- from then on, contract it regularly during your climaxes. We can't guarantee that this will give you multiple orgasms – but it *will* give you pleasant sensations, and a most interesting talking-point with your partner!
- if doing all this has helped you, then you should keep up the regular exercises. That isn't very difficult, because you

can do them unnoticed almost *anywhere* except perhaps in
a nudist colony, or in the men's showers at your local
sports club – where they might perhaps raise an eyebrow
or two . . .

Avoiding obesity

Research in America has shown that men with big bellies
often have poor sex lives, and may indeed become impotent.
Amazingly, if they reduce weight, their love lives often return
to normal.

Add to that the fact that in our own research, women who
are asked to say what they dislike about their partner's
appearance in the bedroom will most often say 'a fat
stomach', and you have two very strong reasons for keeping
your weight down.

Avoiding heavy drinking

In case you haven't noticed, alcohol interferes with the very
delicately balanced process of orgasm. A *little* drink may well
have a desirable 'slowing up' effect on a man. But much more
than that will make it rather difficult for him to get a good
climax, and will blur his senses as well. And a lot of alcohol
will make orgasm totally impossible.

Avoiding smoking

Smoking tends to close down the tubes which carry blood to
the penis, and recent research has strongly linked it to
impotence. Although we have no solid evidence on whether
it affects orgasms, we think that (given the fact that nicotine
exercises its ill-effects on most parts of the body), it's quite
possible that it may.

STEP THREE: MAKE SURE IT'S *SAFE* SEX

Sorry to be spoilsports, but we do think that it's important that as you set out on your new improved orgasmic career, you should practise safe sex.

It's crazy *not* to practise sensible sex these days. Quite apart from AIDS and STDs, there is the little matter of unwanted pregnancy, isn't there? But we also think that unless a guy is very stupid, he is unlikely to enjoy his orgasms to the full in situations which are dangerous. Sure, there is a certain thrill to be gained by doing something risky, and getting away with it.

However, we have never yet had a letter from a man who says 'The greatest orgasm of my life was when I had a quick, unprotected shag with a girl in an alleyway outside the bar where I'd just met her.'

Climaxes in such circumstances are likely to be pretty hurried and unsatisfactory. And, of course, they can have truly disastrous consequences . . .

STEP FOUR: GET THE SETTING RIGHT

In the same way, you're not likely to have wonderful climaxes if you make love in a cold, uncomfortable bedroom, with noise from your neighbours or your parents or your children drifting through the wall.

Poor surroundings will put your partner off, since women are very dependent on having a nice, romantic setting for love-making. But they are also likely to put *you* off, and limit your enjoyment of orgasm.

In particular, the chilly bedrooms which exist in so many Northern countries are real passion-killers when you want to have a climax through oral sex!

You see, it's very difficult to give or receive fellatio when you're freezing to death! (The same applies to cunnilingus.) This is probably why English men and Canadians don't seem to get many of their orgasms through oral sex . . .

So, try and make your bedroom a warm, romantic, comfortable place – a place where your partner will be happy to give you lots of climaxes, and where you will be happy to have them.

STEP FIVE: TEACH YOUR PARTNER WHAT YOU WANT

It's probable that you will not get intensely pleasurable orgasms unless you can persuade your partner to do the things which you like, and which give you the nicest sensations.

Unfortunately, in many countries it's still a fact of life that men and women do not *communicate* much in bed. We have endlessly heard phrases like 'Of course, I couldn't talk to my wife about the way I like my penis rubbed – it would be *much* too embarrassing.'

We think that this crazy lack of communication is responsible for the fact that more than a third of the male respondents to our survey bemoaned the fact that their female partners weren't giving them enough love play!

It seems likely that what a lot of these chaps wanted was oral sex – though undoubtedly many of them just wished to have their penises rubbed by their partners.

Anyway, we implore you (for the sake of your relationship, never mind your orgasms) to tell your partner what really turns you on – and to ask her to do it for you.

It may be that – like some males – you will get your finest climaxes when a woman squeezes her pelvic muscles just before you come. But your lady is not telepathic, so unless you TELL her that you want her to do this, we're afraid that you'll continue to miss out.

STEP SIX: SLOW THINGS UP FOR A BETTER CLIMAX

So far as we are aware, Shere Hite was the first to point out – in her excellent book *The Hite Report on Male Sexuality* – that if a man delays his climax, there's a high chance that that climax will be better.

And, in general, it's true. A rapid orgasm after two minutes of fellatio or hand-play may well be OK, but it's unlikely to be brilliant. In contrast, if you dally with your girlfriend/fiancée/wife/whatever for an agreeable *hour* or so before you finally 'blast away', it is very probable that the orgasm, when it happens, *will be a particularly good one.*

This phenomenon is probably due to the general build-up of male secretions in the sexual area of the body when stimulation is prolonged – coupled perhaps with the effect of pleasurable anticipation in the mind.

Anyway, try it and see what you think. One thing we can tell you is that your partner will almost certainly be grateful . . .

STEP SEVEN: USE FANTASY TOGETHER

There's no doubt that using sexual fantasies can improve the intensity of climaxes, in both men and women. So, provided your partner is agreeable (and studies show that a majority of women are turned on by fantasy) why not arrange with her that from time to time you will both engage in telling each other erotic little fantasies as orgasm approaches? But remember that the fantasy may well make orgasm approach rather *faster* than usual!

However, two quick warnings:

- do not let yourself become 'hooked' on a particular fantasy. Psychologists have found that if a person keeps on thinking about the same thing at the moment of orgasm he may well become addicted to it – and unable to climax without it.
- do not be tempted to turn your fantasies into reality. Wacky erotic stories about sex orgies and mass defloration of Chosen Virgins are one thing in the mind – but quite another thing if a couple are daft enough to start trying them out for real.

STEP EIGHT: MAKE SPECIAL OCCASIONS TOGETHER

It's very easy for orgasms – and, indeed, sex generally – to become very boring and 'run of the mill'. One way you can stop things becoming dull is to organise special sexual occasions. Fortunately, most women *love* such occasions, and will cooperate enthusiastically! As you'll readily appreciate, this will be very nice for you – and for your orgasms . . .

Here are some entertaining special occasions for you to set up:

- a romantic candlelit supper in bed, maybe for an anniversary;
- a massage evening, in which you caress each other languorously for hours before sex;
- a role-play evening, in which you act out the parts of famous sexy lovers;
- a sex-aid night, in which you make one another laugh by

pleasuring each other with wacky devices;
- a delightful, cuddly weekend away;
- a charming picnic in a secluded country spot (and it *has* to be secluded . . .).

STEP NINE: MAKE *HER* HAPPY, TOO

Unless you are a quite extraordinarily selfish and self-centred man, it's very unlikely that you will be able to enjoy tremendous orgasms unless you are making *her* happy, too.

And for full details on how to do this . . . see Chapter Ten.

HOW TO GIVE YOUR MAN BETTER ORGASMS: A GUIDE FOR WOMEN

Don't Do This Unless You Really Want To!

Step One: Understand His Need for Orgasms

Step Two: If He Has Problems with Orgasm, Help Him Deal With Them

Step Three: Give Him Lots of Massage

Step Four: Slow Him Down and Make Him Take His Time

Step Five: Give Him Lots of 'Hand-Play'

Step Six: Give Him Lots of Oral Sex

Step Seven: Talk a Good Orgasm!

Step Eight: Contract Your Pelvic Muscles on Him

Step Nine: Use Fantasy

Step Ten: Use all Available Aids to Erotic Enjoyment!

Step Eleven: Touch Up All His Intimate Places

Step Twelve: Shriek a Lot . . .

DON'T DO THIS UNLESS YOU REALLY WANT TO!

Giving a man better (and more) orgasms is a nice idea, but don't let yourself be pressured into following this guide. Only do it if you *really* want to.

It will mean going in for quite a lot of love-play – including oral sex – and we know that this isn't every woman's cup of tea.

However, we hope that you will find that following our plan is enjoyable, and frankly, we think that in return your man should study Chapter Ten, which gives a similar guide to how males can improve WOMEN'S orgasms!

STEP ONE: UNDERSTANDING HIS NEED FOR ORGASMS

It's vital to appreciate that men – or, at any rate, most men – are far more orgasm-orientated than women are. *You* may often feel like a nice, romantic love-making session which makes you feel wanted and loved. *He* mainly wants to come!

Be prepared for the fact that men tend to do crazy things like *counting* orgasms, or even rating them from one to ten on a sort of sexual Richter scale.

Indeed, some younger guys freely admit that as they're having one climax, they're thinking 'How soon can I get another one?'

So, don't underestimate your man's desire for climaxes. This chapter will tell you how to give them to him.

STEP TWO: IF HE HAS PROBLEMS WITH ORGASM, HELP HIM DEAL WITH THEM

It's as well to remember at the outset that a huge number of men have minor problems with orgasm – for example, in our survey we found that six out of ten males admitted that they have a bit of a tendency to come too soon. (And orgasms are never really very good when you come too soon.)

Other men have more severe difficulties – like full-blown premature ejaculation or ejaculatory incompetence (in which a man cannot climax inside a woman).

So if your man has any orgasmic difficulties at all – even if it's just a habit of firing off too quickly – it's a good idea to get these sorted out right away. Methods of doing so are explained in Chapter Fourteen.

STEP THREE: GIVE HIM LOTS OF MASSAGE

We strongly recommend massage as a way of pepping up your partner's orgasm – and it may do yours no harm, either. Having a session twice a week will pay rich dividends!

Gentle, unhurried, loving massage is a really good method of:

- relaxing the male body and easing its aches and pains;
- turning it on sexually.

This is one reason why girls in topless parlours do genuinely give their clients a soothing massage of the muscles before getting down to sexual stimulation.

So, we suggest the following:

- get yourself a bottle of massage oil from a pharmacy;
- make sure that the bedroom is nice and warm;

- strip off completely – and strip him off, too;
- ask him to lie on his face;
- starting with his neck – which is often very tense in both men and women – give him a really thorough massage with your palms and fingertips, gradually working down past his buttocks to his calves;
- then turn him over, and again work down from his neck to his ankles;
- but leave his penis till last – you'll probably find that massaging it leads straight into sex . . .

STEP FOUR: SLOW HIM DOWN AND MAKE HIM TAKE HIS TIME

A simple fact of life is that male orgasm – and probably female orgasm, too – is very much more intense *if it is long-delayed.*

As we said a moment ago, an orgasm which happens very quickly is not likely to be a terrifically good one, but if you make your man build up a gradual 'head of steam' over a period of thirty, forty-five or sixty minutes, then when his climax happens it's quite likely to be a shattering one.

So . . . tease him a bit. Take him up to the brink, and then ease off a little. Give him a minute or two of rest before you start again. Finally, go for it and watch the explosive results.

Please note that you ought to explain to him *first* what you're going to do! Otherwise, he may be a bit puzzled (and frustrated) by all this starting and stopping.

STEP FIVE: GIVE HIM LOTS OF 'HAND-PLAY'

You may have noticed that in our survey, a very substantial

number of men say that they don't get enough love-play from
their partners.

You might be surprised by that finding, but (getting down
to basics) what it means is that they want more hand-play
and more oral sex! So, use your hands to give his penis and
his balls lots of caresses. If you don't know how this is done,
then just ask him what he likes. You'll almost certainly find
that he prefers the sort of finger-rubbing which he's been
used to since he started 'rubbing himself up' at the age of
thirteen or fourteen.

If you have a look at Figure 11.4, back in Chapter Eleven,
that'll give you a good idea of the sort of thing we mean.

Whether you take him all the way to orgasm by hand-play
is up to you, and him. In fact, most men like a *mixture* of
climaxes – some through hand-play, some through oral sex,
and some through intercourse.

But if you can get really skilled at hand-play, and learn to
exert gentle pressure on his shaft *just as he is coming*, then
you will find that you can give him extraordinarily intense
orgasms.

We recommend that the two of you spend several years in
experimenting with this technique . . .

STEP SIX: GIVE HIM LOTS OF ORAL SEX

Men absolutely love this. To say that it's a major talking-point
in the letters they send us is the under statement of the year.
('Dear Christine, I am writing to you to tell you that my wife
does not give me enough oral sex . . .')

Fortunately, these days the great majority of women –
especially younger women – are very happy to give fellatio to
a loving partner. If you've never done it, we can assure you
that it's worth learning. You can make a start by imitating
Figure 11.6, back in Chapter Eleven. From then on, be

guided by what your man tells you feels good for him. Do *not* scrape him with your teeth – this is a real passion-killer.

The two of you probably won't go all the way to orgasm on every occasion you go in for fellatio. But even if you don't, this is a great way for really working a man up and driving him wild – so that whichever way he eventually comes, he should have an excellent climax.

However, if from time to time you want him to have his orgasm during fellatio itself then you will need to develop your oral techniques in order to make it all a success.

To be honest, this will take some months or even years of experiment together, but you'll get there in the end (so to speak). What we recommend is that you practise hard at closing your mouth very *tightly* around the shaft of his penis, because this increases the strength of the sensation as orgasm approaches.

Just before his climax, it's also a good idea if you suck strongly, and also try to use your tongue to 'swirl' round his shaft.

One note of caution: many men's penises become very *tender* just a moment after coming (just like many women's clitorises do). If this is the case with your guy, you really do need to stop sucking and licking *at the instant you realise that he has come.*

STEP SEVEN: TALK A GOOD ORGASM!

You can give your man more exciting orgasms – and probably get him to climax more frequently – if you turn him on by *talking* to him in bed.

Amazingly, our studies show that an awful lot of couples (particularly older ones) don't actually speak to each other during sex! This is crazy. No wonder so many of them have communication problems . . .

In contrast, women who are skilled at really turning men on have learned that it's a good idea to say raunchy things in bed. You can say whatever you like: tell him little erotic stories; explain how excited, moist, dripping (or whatever) you are; or praise his penis – men like this a great deal.

Depending on what the two of you are comfortable with, you may choose to use the traditional Anglo-Saxon 'four letter words'. Be warned that a few men are very put off by hearing a woman saying such things; but these days, many males are driven quite wild by the sound of a female voice murmuring 'Fuck me harder, darling' as they go into orgasm.

STEP EIGHT: CONTRACT YOUR PELVIC MUSCLES ON HIM

This is something you can do during intercourse to increase stimulation and make his climax even better. You'll enjoy it, too.

Your pelvic muscles are like a sort of 'collar' round your vagina, and a few inches up it. So if you 'twitch' them during sexual intercourse, you will grip his penis – usually somewhere about halfway up the shaft.

This is like a special intimate massage to his cock, and he should be very grateful to you for doing it!

Learning to contract your pelvic muscles is easy. (It's the same trick which many women have been taught to do after childbirth, in order to prevent them from getting a prolapse, or 'fallen womb'.) You just make a conscious and very deliberate effort to 'tweak' the muscles which stop you passing urine. That's it.

When you do it during intercourse, a reasonable plan is to twitch and release a number of times as he comes up to his climax. Bear in mind that the tweaking will probably make him orgasm rather faster, because this is a very exciting feeling for him. So obviously, you need to use this highly erotic caress with some care.

Over the years, we have heard persistent rumours of women who have learned – allegedly in Eastern temples! – to use *two* sets of muscles, one after the other, thus exercising a delightful 'milking' effect on a lover's penis.

Sadly, we have never encountered such a lady. But if you, dear reader, can achieve this amazing feat of muscular coordination, we think you deserve some sort of medal.

STEP NINE: USE FANTASY

It's certainly worth using sexual fantasies to pep up your partner's orgasms – and your own. Concocting some wonderfully raunchy scenario will give him a more intense and more enjoyable orgasm. For instance, you could agree to pretend that he is just a virgin lad, and that you are an experienced older woman, seducing him for the first time.

Or – very popular this – you can pretend to be some famous film star who he really fancies. It's surprisingly easy to act the part of Madonna or Nicole Kidman, particularly in the dark.

With the more mature man, Marilyn Monroe or Jane Russell often go down very well . . .

STEP TEN: USE ALL AVAILABLE AIDS TO EROTIC ENJOYMENT!

Yes, make this one your 'Mission Statement', as the people who're into management jargon love to say . . .

It's worth trying any aids you can find which turn on your

man – and indeed yourself. We're not just talking about sex aids here, though they may be useful in boosting orgasm – particularly if you can find intimate places to put a vibrator just as he comes . . .

No, we also mean things like:

- erotic 'talking books': amazingly, these little cassettes, often read by distinguished actors and actresses, have proved immensely popular since they were introduced in about 1994;
- erotic novels: obviously, stick to the legal ones. Reading one to your partner as you stimulate him (or as you make love, if you can manage it!) can be a wild turn-on for your man;
- erotic videos: again, stay within the law – but perfectly legal saucy films have become widespread 'aids to orgasm' in the 1990s. Indeed, in the 1995 University of Chicago study, 23 per cent of American men and 11 per cent of American women said that they'd bought such videos in the last year. However, we personally think that you should keep away from anything that might be exploitative of actresses – or actors.

A curious fact which has emerged from our research is that many couples use these audio tapes, books and films *in such a way that when the characters in the story reach orgasm, so do the couple in the bed.* We must admit that this could be a good way of boosting the orgasmic pleasure of either sex.

STEP ELEVEN: TOUCH UP ALL HIS INTIMATE PLACES

To get him going, and to give added 'oomph' to his climax, you'll find it useful to let your fingertips trail into and around all the secret, intimate places of his body. We'd particularly recommend:

- behind his ears;
- in his arm-pits;
- behind his knees;
- on and *under* his scrotum (bearing in mind that most men almost unconsciously caress themselves there when they masturbate);
- his nipples;
- in the 'cleavage' between his buttocks.

How far you take this last caress is up to you, but we should point out that there are hygiene risks *unless* you wash your hand immediately afterwards. But many women exploit this particular 'stroke' to the full, using it to drive their menfolk wild and spur them on to orgasm.

Furthermore, if you penetrate deeper (using a *lubricated* finger, please!), you can – as you probably know – stimulate his prostate gland by rubbing it gently with your fingertip.

In many males, this will help produce an extraordinarily intense and quite unusual orgasm – in which the seminal fluid can come out with remarkable velocity and shoot a surprisingly long way!

Research-minded women may actually be able to *feel* the contractions of their lovers' prostates with their fingertips at the moment of climax.

STEP TWELVE: SHRIEK A LOT

Most men love to hear this – particularly as they're coming. So whether you're climaxing yourself at that particular moment or not, give it a try. Good luck.